What's Fair? Anthology

SERIES EDITORS
Margaret Iveson
Samuel Robinson

EDITORIAL CONSULTANT
Alan Simpson

LITERATURE CONSULTANT
Rivka Cranley

TEACHER CONSULTANTS
Flora Miller
Kathy Bell
David Crichton
Judy Thorne

PRENTICE HALL CANADA INC.

ISBN 0-13-020256-8
© 1993 by Prentice-Hall Canada Inc., Scarborough, Ontario
ALL RIGHTS RESERVED

No part of this book may be reproduced in any form without permission in
writing from the publishers.

Anthologists: Todd Mercer, Linda Sheppard
Researchers: Monika Croydon, Catherine Rondina

A Ligature Book
Cover Illustration: Baby Face by Michael Deas

Canadian Cataloguing in Publication Data
Main entry under title:

What's Fair? : anthology

(MultiSource)
ISBN 0-13-020256-8

1. Fairness – Literary collections. 2. Children's
literature. I. Iveson, Margaret L., 1948–   .
II. Robinson, Sam, 1937–   . III. Series.
PZ5.W483 1993   j808.8'0355   C92-095218-6

Printed and bound in Canada

Nobody can make you feel
inferior without your consent.

ELEANOR ROOSEVELT
(1884–1962)
AMERICAN STATESWOMAN

Contents

"And the LUCKY WINNER IS..."

A short story
by Monica Hughes

The heliolites soared above the river valley, clustering, separating.

To Jon, squinting up into the sunshine, they were like a cloud of brilliant butterflies. For just a moment he wished he were up there with them, but only for a moment. The one time he'd soared he'd felt so nauseated that he'd barely made it back to solid earth in one piece. The nausea, along with a hatred of crowds, seemed to be the flipside of his "gift." He'd gladly trade the shameful hidden skill of telekinesis for the chance to soar with his sister and his best friend. To be skilled in telepathy and telekinesis, gifts useful only to spies and other servants of the state, was a burden he would happily cast off. To be like Peri. To be free . . .

Peri, strapped in her harness, watched the city swing beneath her, a slowly rotating jigsaw of ceramic roofs, solar panels and streets, with the river cutting a random furrow through its geometric order. Directly below her she could see Jon, a dark dot on the field by the bridge. Kid brother, isolated as usual from the crowd.

She felt the chill of cloud-shadow on her cheek an instant before her heliolite lost power. Automatically she compensated, maneuvering neatly into the thermal that rose from the hot ground of the bluffs above the river. Around her the others moved smoothly into place on the funnel of warm air.

This was the best moment, soaring like a bird in the silence of the thermal. Without worry, at one with the air, she swung in her harness, leaning into the thermal, following it around. She forgot about her math test, so awful, but totally essential if she could ever hope to work in the space program, about her brother Jon, more silent and separate from their friends every day, about Nev. Did Nev really love her as much as she loved him? As much as he said . . . Or was it really only a Senior Year relationship that meant no more to him than trying to beat her at squash or soaring? Everything was left behind in the wrinkled land below, as Peri soared in the silence.

Then the sun slid from behind an obscuring cloud to reactivate the tiny engines on the wing tips. She engaged the jets and soared out of the thermal, away from the crowd, up, up, to that breathtaking instant before stalling. Then she plunged and regained speed in a shiver of nylon wings. It was a tricky maneuver, one she had just perfected. Up here she was the best, and it felt good.

Over her shoulder Peri glanced at the others, just breaking free of the thermal like a cluster of firework stars. Something was badly wrong! One heliolite seemed to hesitate at the thermal interface, shuddered and plunged suddenly toward the ground. She saw its colour, a royal blue zagged with a lightning line of gold. Nev's! In a single frozen instant she saw the tiny figure of Jon scurry across the field. Do something, Jon! her mind screamed. Reach out with your telekinesis. Grab him. Defy gravity. You can do it! But Jon wasn't God, and Nev's heliolite continued to spin downward like a twisting maple key. Instinctively Peri cut the power to her props and followed it down in a steep frantic dive.

The nylon shivered and the wind screamed through the titanium frame as she approached the ground. She could see Nev's 'lite, broken below her, Jon running towards it. Now the ground was rushing towards her. She soared briefly to absorb speed and, in a series of roller coaster moves, came to a stop fifty meters away. Her fingers fumbled stiffly at the harness buckles. Come on. Come on. At last she was able to wriggle free, to run stiff-legged across the rough turf towards the broken heliolite. The fifty meters seemed forever.

"Nev! Nev!" She stumbled in the grass and Jon caught her arm.

"He's alive, Peri. I can still sense his life force. But . . ."

Nev lay still. His eyes were not quite closed and she could see a glint of white between the lids. He looked horribly not there, as if the Nev she knew were in some other place and this was only a shell.

The medics arrived, to slip a rigid collar around his neck, to ease a stretcher sheet under his body, wrapping him carefully and light-zapping the sheet to stiffness. She watched the cocoon that was Nev loaded aboard, watched the copter take off. Then she stood numbly, with the wind drying her lips, until Jon put his arm around her and helped her climb to the top of the bluffs, where the others waited outside the heliolite rental agency.

They crowded around. "What happened?" "What went wrong?" "How's Nev?" But there were no answers.

Hours later, in the hospital, Peri tried to explain to Nev's mother what had gone wrong. "We'd been trying out a new maneuver. I guess he didn't . . ." She stammered and was silent under the contempt in Mrs. Wright's eyes.

"If it hadn't been for you . . . you're always leading him on with your reckless ideas. Those crazy heliolites—they should be banned. What if he dies? What if he never walks again? Oh . . . oh . . ."

Peri flinched from her anger and her pain. "I'm sorry, Mrs. Wright. I'd give anything in the world for this not to have happened."

"Why do you want to do these crazy things? How come you can't be more like your brother? For all he's a year younger than you, he's got more sense, he's not so foolish as to . . ."

"That's not fair, Mrs. Wright." Jon stood protectively in front of Peri. "Nev's every bit as crazy about helioliting as Peri, honestly."

Then the doctor came and there were involved explanations about the realities of spinal cord injuries. Nev's mother began to cry, her mouth open in an ugly square.

Peri swallowed her own tears. "Oh, please don't cry, Mrs. Wright. It'll be all right. They've got new techniques. Microsurgery and electric stimulation. It'll be okay." She turned to the authority in sparkling white, the silver caduceus winking in his left lapel. "Isn't that true, doctor? Tell her."

"Indeed, we have made amazing advances in the field of nerve regeneration in the last twenty years. Biochemistry. Electrical stimulation. It's a very lengthy process, of course. Labour intensive. Expensive."

Mrs. Wright twisted her fingers together. "I've got medical coverage. That'll take care of it, doctor."

"Your insurance will certainly cover the tests we've done so far and your son's stay in hospital for the next few days. You need have no concern on that account. Beyond that . . . well, talk to your insurance agent. You're looking at something in the neighbourhood of a quarter of a million dollars." The doctor's buzzer beeped.

"A quarter of a . . ."

"Excuse me. We'll have an opportunity to talk later. In the meantime, a visit to the accounting office will make procedures clearer to you."

He hurried away, leaving them standing in the middle of the waiting room.

Mrs. Wright turned on Peri, her mouth tight. "See what you've done. You've ruined both our lives with your stupid reckless games. A quarter of a million! How will I ever . . .?" She scrubbed her eyes angrily. "Oh, go away. Get out!"

Peri tried to protest, but Jon took her arm and pulled her along the corridor and through the doors into the sunlit grounds of the hospital. "Don't cry. Don't pay attention to her. It's not your fault."

"Perhaps it is. I'm much better aloft than Nev. But he always wanted to catch up."

"It was his choice. You didn't twist his arm."

"Maybe I could leave school and get a job. Just to help pay for Nev's treatment."

"Mum and Dad'll never let you. Not in a million years. Besides, what about the space program?"

"That doesn't matter. Nothing matters except Nev getting better. Oh, Jon, what are we going to do?"

Peri put on a bright face to visit the hospital the next day, but it slipped off at the sight of Nev cradled in a paraplegic bed.

"Nev, I'm so sorry. It's all my fault."

He managed a grin. "You sound just like my Mom! I told her and I'm telling you and then let's forget about it, okay. I wasn't trying to copy your crazy stunt, I'm not that dumb. One of the struts snapped, that's all."

"Are you sure?" Relief flooded through her, followed by shame that it should make a difference. After all, it didn't help Nev a bit whether it was her fault or not.

"Quite sure. And the doctor had a bit of good news. Something called the Hi-med Lottery Fund. To help poor slobs like me who can't come up with a quarter of a million to get my legs back."

"Then it's okay?"

"Not exactly okay. But my National Security Number goes into the lottery locally for a bed in the neurological unit here. Every time there's a draw I get a chance."

"There can't be that many people with spinal cord injuries right here in town. The odds must be pretty good, don't you think?"

"I'm betting on it." Nev managed a grin and she grabbed his hand and held it against her cheek, turning her face away so he shouldn't see her tears.

When visiting time was up, Peri went in search of the doctor whose name was on the chart at the foot of Nev's bed. She found him in the cafeteria, coffee cup in hand.

"Please, can I talk to you about one of your patients, Nev Wright?"

"Are you a member of the family?"

"N . . . no. Not exactly."

"Then I can't discuss the patient with you."

"It's not that. I mean, I don't want to ask you about Nev. But the program . . . the lottery?"

"Yes? Do sit down, Miss . . . er . . ."

"Peri Stanley. I don't understand how the lottery works."

"It's an experimental program. A real step forward in the democratization of medicine, we believe. Any major procedure or experimental protocol consuming over a hundred thousand dollars in excess of medical insurance coverage is supported by the province, the clients being chosen by lottery."

"Yes, I know that bit. But how does it actually work?"

"Nev's National Security Number will be submitted to the city lottery foundation. Every month, during the regular drawings for prizes in the provincial lottery, several numbers are drawn randomly from those submitted by the City hospital system. If Nev's number is drawn, then his worries are over. Free medical treatment, physiotherapy, whatever's needed to get the boy back on his feet."

"And the odds, doctor? What are Nev's chances?" Peri burst out.

"There are enough funds to admit three persons a month to the centre."

Three people? Out of how many? There can't be that many people with spinal cord injuries."

"You'd be surprised. Several hundred. Of course he can try again, up to two years. The chances of rehabilitation after that time become minimal."

"Three out of several hundred?" Peri choked on the words.

"Better than nothing." The doctor smiled wryly and got to his feet. "And you can always try to raise the money yourselves. People do, you know. Bake sales, marathons, that sort of thing. Excuse me, I must go. Good luck."

Luck, thought Peri miserably as she left the hospital. That's what it's going to take. Monumental, stupendous luck. Then she stopped so suddenly that the door swung against her shoulders as the person behind her pushed through.

"Pardon me."

"Sorry." Peri walked back home, her mind furiously going over the possibility. Jon. And his gift for telekinesis. Moving things with his mind. Small things, like dice. Or maybe the numbers in a lottery?

"You're crazy!" was Jon's reaction.

"You can change the odds, Jon, you know you can."

"But that's cheating, Peri. I won't cheat. And suppose someone found out. Can you imagine what my life'd be like if I ever let people know what I can do? The Government'd probably draft me or use me in experiments. I wouldn't have a life of my own. It'd be horrible."

"I know telekinesis is rare, but don't you think you're a bit paranoid about the Government. After all . . ."

"I've heard stories of people simply vanishing. Sucked into the system to be used. After all, Peri, they use dolphins to carry bombs and mines. Why should they be more fussy about people?"

Peri wrapped her arms around her chest and shivered. "I know, Jon," she said in a small voice. "But what about Nev?"

That was it, wasn't it? Jon thought gloomily, after he'd got away from his sister's pleading. What about Nev? He found himself reliving the nightmare moment when he realized that the heliolite was out of control, that his telekinetic power was useless, that he could no more stop the falling heliolite than he could stop the spin of Earth.

But now there was something he could do. Change the

odds in the provincial lottery and undo the damage that his failure to help Nev had caused.

It's wrong, an inner voice told him clearly. Once you start using your powers to cheat, there's no end to it, is there?

Yes, but this is different.

No, it isn't. It's no different from always winning at backgammon, even if you don't try to throw double sixes.

His mind seesawed miserably to and fro between the opposite and irreconcilable facts, and he found himself hating Peri for having had the stupid brilliant idea in the first place.

Three days later the ambulance brought Nev home to his mother's apartment in the same block where Jon and Peri's family lived. He arrived in a flesh-coloured, permeable plastic body cast and a variable slant chair-bed.

Jon tried a light touch. "You're looking great. Apart from that bruise on your forehead." Stupid, he thought savagely. That the best you can do?

"And apart from being numb from the hips down I guess I'll survive." Nev sounded just as unreal.

"You'll be into rehab in no time," Peri burst out. "I've had this fabulous idea to beat the odds so that your number will come up right away."

"How are you going to do that, Mata Hari? You can't seduce the robot that runs the lottery—or can you?"

"Oh, don't be such an idiot. Telekinesis."

"You, Peri? You've got as much psi ability as a plasti-brick wall."

"She's thinking of me, Nev. It's crazy. The numbers are probably generated in a computer concealed in a sealed vault somewhere."

"But they aren't, Jon." Colour flooded Nev's face. "I asked about it in hospital. The lottery's run in public, with a live audience, and one of those old-fashioned bingo machines that throw up the numbers randomly. Anyone can go and watch. Mostly they give out prizes, but they run the Hi-med Lottery at the same time."

"Nev, are you saying you think it'll work? You really want me to try it?"

"Of course he does," Peri shouted at him. "You can't not. Jon, you're my one and only brother, but I swear I'll never talk to you again if you don't at least try to help Nev."

"Take it easy, Peri. Back off. It's Jon's decision." Nev interrupted.

"I don't even know if I can do it to order, or if it's like dreams, something that just happens."

"It'll be okay, Jon. I'll help you practise. All we need to start working is Nev's National Security Number." She pushed up his sleeve and ran her thumb over the digits tattooed there. "24-2-30 . . . your birthday. I remember that part. Four days before mine. Then 005193 . . . right?"

"Eleven numbers. Think you can handle that many, Jon?"

"I dunno, Nev. But I can try."

Now that the choice was out of his hands, Jon pushed the guilt and worry to the back of his head and concentrated on honing his telekinetic powers. Peri wrote the numbers zero through nine over and over again on table tennis balls and put them in an antique pickling jar that their mother used as a vase, and Jon began to practise plucking out the digits of Nev's security number in order. After three weeks Jon had a permanent headache and Peri was nervous enough to jump out of her skin.

"It's no good. My brain's turning to mush, and my psi abilities aren't getting any better. Like I said in the beginning—I don't think it's a thing you can force." Jon sighed. "I'm afraid it's hopeless."

"It's my fault. I've been pushing you too hard. Why don't you take a rest. After all it's three days . . ." Her voice wobbled. "Three whole days till the lottery."

Peri and Jon waited in line outside the convention centre until the doors were opened and the crowd pushed in.

"We've got to get close to the front." Jon warned her.

"I know." Peri gasped, the wind knocked out of her as an elbow-jabbing woman pushed past them.

They managed to get seats in the front row close to the enormous number-generating machine. It was edged with garish fluorescent lights, red, orange, blue and purple, which flashed on and off in rhythm with the latest hyperpunk.

Jon groaned. "It'll be hard to concentrate with all that going on."

Peri squeezed his arm. "You'll manage. I know you will." She turned, so he wouldn't see her face and guess how nervous she really was, and stared around the hall.

The seats were filling up fast. Streamers hung from the ceiling, twisting in the air-conditioning. LOTTO-LOTTOLOTTO they spelled endlessly. The crowd noises rose to beat the hyperpunk. The lights flashed. She could feel the tension zapping at her nerves, tightening her skin. Her stomach flipped uneasily.

"Surely not all these people have friends needing help?" She turned back to Jon.

"I'll bet not one of them is here for the Hi-med Lottery. Take a look at the program."

"Win a Mazda hovercraft . . . a home fusion unit . . . but this isn't what we're here for."

"Down near the end." Jon pointed. "Three rehabilitation places at Healing Hands Medical Unit. Just before drawing the numbers for the Provincial Lottery. That's what everyone's here for, I guess, the big prize—a tax-free year for the whole family."

As he spoke the lights and sound mercifully dimmed and the Master of Ceremonies glided out into the spotlight, a smoothfaced android familiar to Peri from news and weather reports on the local channel. There'd been an occasion, Peri heard a woman in the row behind her whisper, when an irate loser had gunned down the lottery MC, so it was no longer a favoured post for a human, despite the publicity. If there should be another incident, well, androids were replaceable.

"Welcome to the twenty-ninth running of the new provincial lottery. I hope you all have your National Security Numbers on you—har-har. Today it may be your turn to win a home composter, a water purification unit, a super hovercraft. And, as I'm sure you all know, the big prize today is . . ."

"Jon, what about . . .?"

"Sh. He'll get to it. Just listen."

"And folks, between the draws for the home composter and the big prize, we will, as usual, draw three places for hospital beds in the rehab unit of the City Hospital. The lucky winners will receive the very latest in scientific treatment absolutely free! So come on, all you folks here and at home watching this programme—brought to you by the makers of NoZone, the cream that guarantees freedom from skin cancer—let's begin our evening of fun and excitement."

An hour and a half dragged by for Peri and Jon. The numbered balls flipped up and down on the current of air in the machine. Randomly one would pop out, and Smoothface would announce the number. As the eleventh and final number popped out, the central computer searched out the name and telephone of the lucky winner. Within a minute the audience was treated to a display of hysterical joy, brought by home videophone to the big screen above the stage. Instant win. Instant emotion. Between the draws the audience ate sushi and fried squid.

"Look, Jon. Something's happening."

Two workwomen in coveralls, who probably earned less in a year than Smoothface's owner earned in a night, wheeled on a smaller machine, decorated with fluorescent H's, which blinked frenetically on and off.

" . . . and now, folks, for those unfortunate few who have suffered traumatic accidents in the past year, the City Hospital's Hi-med Lottery brings you the Healing Hands Hope Chest! In this transparent container," Smoothface went on, "are the National Security Numbers of all those poor folks in need of a boost—a boost which we intend to give them tonight."

Peri could see that each of the balls in this container was much larger, large enough to have an entire NS number printed on its sides. This was going to be totally different from extracting the right digit from zero to nine, and getting it right eleven times. Finding the ball with Nev's number on it within a container of several hundred was like pinpointing one star in a galaxy with one's eyes shut.

"Jon, what'll we do?" She grabbed his arm.

"It's the dregs, I know. But I'll try just visualizing Nev's number and willing it up. Maybe it'll work. Maybe we'll have to call this a practice run for the next lottery, or the one after."

"But . . ."

Jon was no longer listening. He closed his eyes. Peri could see the muscle at the corner of his jaw quiver and tense. She doubled her fists in her lap so that the nails dug into the palms.

The balls began to bounce on the current of air within the machine, rattling as they moved randomly around. She stared and caught her breath in a gasp. Up the near rim of the container a single ball wriggled upward, against gravity, to bob on the air stream. She looked quickly around. Had anyone else noticed the unusual movement?

Most of the audience had left the stands for a drink of lo-al beer and a sushi snack. To them, this was the boring interlude before the main event. Those who remained were talking, joking, rustling their programs. Some twisted theirs into paper airplanes and glided them towards the stage. Peri looked anxiously at Jon. Would this nonsense distract him? But it was all right. His eyes were still shut, concentrating.

Then she saw her. A woman dead centre in the front row was staring intently at the machine. Peri remembered her. The woman who'd jabbed her out of the way as they had jostled in the doorway. She could still feel the bruise on her ribs.

In a sea of munching mouths, her face stood out. Her eyes were narrowed, her forehead furrowed. She looked as if she wasn't even breathing.

Peri's eyes darted back to the number generator. Another ball was creeping up the side. It spun against the one she guessed that Jon was guiding and hovered beneath the narrow exit passage. Jon's ball jostled it, they spun apart and, as they ricochetted off the walls of the container, a third ball was hiccuped into the exit and rolled into the MC's outstretched hand.

". . . and the lucky winner is . . . 91-07-13-02547. In one moment we will see for ourselves . . ." A picture flashed onto the screen. A lean man propped in a wheelchair, neckbrace forcing his chin up, someone's hand holding the phone to his ear. Smoothface spoke into his mike. "Mr. James Rierdon. I guess they'll be calling you lucky Jim tonight, eh, Mr. Rierdon? Free rehabilitation at the city hospital! Congratulations and big hand for Mr. Rierdon!"

As the screen blanked out there was a spatter of applause and then the crowd noise filled the hall like the wind against a diving heliolite. The balls began to bubble on their air jet. Up and over. Down and up. Again one ball edged up to the surface, stayed there, fighting gravity. A second ball rose beside it.

Like two gladiators in the ring, thought Peri. Each feinting, watching the other's move, ready to block it, to be the first beneath the narrow exit. She saw the MC's hand move. Both balls rolled towards the opening. And jammed. Neither gave a millimeter. Sweat ran down Jon's face. Six seats to her right Peri saw the woman's face glisten pallidly under the bright lights.

"Sorry, folks." Smoothface smacked the side of the old machine. The woman's body jolted as if she had been hit. Peri heard Jon grunt in pain. "Little jam-up here," the android went on. "A bit more air to stir them up again and . . . here we are. The lucky winner is 15-11-03-47892!"

Once more a picture flashed on the screen, this time of a woman in her mid twenties lying in a quadriplegic's harness.

"Congratulations on your win, Daisy Jones. Daisy's been waiting for electrotherapy and nerve surgery for a long eight months following a car accident. Remember, folks, your driving safety depends on a good computer program. Keep your module checked!"

Their opponent's face was dead white. She looked as if she might faint any second now. If she does, a small ugly voice said clearly in Peri's head, then we've got it made. Now she knew that Jon had the mental strength and the skill to pull Nev's number up. Third time lucky . . .

But Jon was on his feet, grabbing Peri's arm. "We're getting out of here."

"What's the matter? You're so near . . ."

At the door he turned and waited. The MC's smooth voice reached them faintly. " . . . and the lucky winner is . . . baby Alison Temple. Baby Alison was born with severe cerebral palsy. Now, with the latest techniques of muscle and nerve rehabilitation . . ." His voice was lost in a torrent of laughter and sobs. "Ladies and gentlemen, right here in the audience, here is Mrs. Temple, little Alison's mother! What a moment! Mrs. Temple, would you like to tell us exactly what you're feeling right now . . ."

Jon put his arm through Peri's and pulled her through the crowd, past the stalls selling lucky T-shirts, stuffed bean cakes, four-leafed clovers and vials of moon dust. Tears ran down Peri's face and she brushed them away angrily.

They walked on until they came to the footbridge across the river. It was hung with paper lanterns, and the pleasure boats beneath looked like illuminated water beetles. Here Jon stopped.

"I could read that woman's thoughts, Peri. So strong. I could see her baby, and what treatment could do for her.

I'm sorry. I'm really sorry. And it'd be the same the next time round, the next lottery, wouldn't it? Always the knowledge that if we cheated so Nev's number would come up it'd be at someone else's expense."

"How are you going to tell him?" Her angry tears splashed on the parapet. "What's the use of your esper skills if you can't even help Nev? I just hate you, Jon!"

He looked away from her anger, staring absently down at the strings of lights reflected in the water. They blinked on and off. White. Red. Green. Idly he switched the order. Red. White. Green. And back again. Suddenly he straightened up and whistled. His eyes sparkled. "Maybe I can do something for Nev after all, Peri." He walked quickly away from her through the brightly dressed crowd.

Three months later, when Peri and Jon were making their daily visit to Nev's apartment after school, Nev grinned at Jon. "I think you can tell her now."

"Really?"

"Tell me what? Hey, you two, what's been going on?"

"I got the idea on the bridge that night, the lottery night, looking down at the coloured lights. And it made me think about the damaged nerves in Nev's spine. And whether telekinesis would be useful. So I went to the medical library and did some reading, and . . . well, anyway, Nev and I've been working on it for the last while."

"Working on what?"

"This."

Slowly, thoughtfully, Nev wiggled his toes.

THE CAGED BIRD IN SPRINGTIME

What can it be,
This curious anxiety?
It is as if I wanted
To fly away from here.

But how absurd!
I have never flown in my life,
And I do not know
What flying means, though I have heard,
Of course, something about it.

Why do I peck the wires of this little cage?
It is the only nest I have ever known.
But I want to build my own,
High in the secret branches of the air.

I cannot quite remember how
It is done, but I know
That what I want to do
Cannot be done here.

I have all I need—
Seed and water, air and light.
Why, then, do I weep with anguish,
And beat my head and my wings
Against those sharp wires, while the children
Smile at each other, saying: 'Hark how he sings'?

JAMES KIRKUP

The
NECKLACE

A classic short story by the French author
Guy de Maupassant

She was one of those pretty and charming girls, born, as
if by an accident of fate, into a family of clerks. With no
dowry, no prospects, no way of any kind of being met,
understood, loved, and married by a man both prosper-
ous and famous, she was finally married to a minor clerk
in the Ministry of Education.

She dressed plainly because she could not afford fine
clothes, but was as unhappy as a woman who has come
down in the world; for women have no family rank or
social class. With them, beauty, grace, and charm take the
place of birth and breeding. Their natural poise, their
instinctive good taste, and their mental cleverness are the
sole guiding principles which make daughters of the common people the equals of ladies in high society.

She grieved incessantly, feeling that she had been born
for all the little niceties and luxuries of living. She grieved

over the shabbiness of her apartment, the dinginess of the walls, the worn-out appearance of the chairs, the ugliness of the draperies. All these things, which another woman of her class would not even have noticed, gnawed at her and made her furious. The sight of the little Breton girl who did her humble housework roused in her disconsolate regrets and wild daydreams. She would dream of silent chambers, draped with Oriental tapestries and lighted by tall bronze floor lamps, and of two handsome butlers in knee breeches, who, drowsy from the heavy warmth cast by the central stove, dozed in large overstuffed armchairs.

She would dream of great reception halls hung with old silks, of fine furniture filled with priceless curios, and of small, stylish, scented sitting rooms just right for the four o'clock chat with intimate friends, with distinguished and sought-after men whose attention every woman envies and longs to attract.

When dining at the round table, covered for the third day with the same cloth, opposite her husband, who would raise the cover of the soup tureen, declaring delightedly, "Ah! a good stew! There's nothing I like better . . ." she would dream of fashionable dinner parties, of gleaming silverware, of tapestries making the walls alive with characters out of history and strange birds in a fairyland forest; she would dream of delicious dishes served on wonderful china, of gallant compliments whispered and listened to with a sphinxlike smile as one eats the rosy flesh of a trout or nibbles at the wings of a grouse.

She had no evening clothes, no jewels, nothing. But those were the things she wanted; she felt that was the kind of life for her. She so much longed to please, be envied, be fascinating and sought after.

She had a well-to-do friend, a classmate of convent-school days whom she would no longer go to see, simply because she would feel so distressed on returning home. And she would weep for days on end from vexation, regret, despair, and anguish.

Then one evening, her husband came home proudly holding out a large envelope.

"Look," he said, "I've got something for you."

She excitedly tore open the envelope and pulled out a printed card bearing these words:

"The Minister of Education and Mme. Georges Ramponneau beg M. and Mme. Loisel to do them the honor of attending an evening reception at the Ministerial Mansion on Friday, January 18."

Instead of being delighted, as her husband had hoped, she scornfully tossed the invitation on the table, murmuring, "What good is that to me?"

"But, my dear, I thought you'd be thrilled to death. You never get a chance to go out, and this is a real affair, a wonderful one! I had an awful time getting a card. Everybody wants one; it's much sought after, and not many clerks have a chance at one. You'll see all the most important people there."

She gave him an irritated glance and burst out impatiently, "What do you think I have to go in?"

He hadn't given that a thought. He stammered, "Why, the dress you wear when we go to the theater. That looks quite nice, I think."

He stopped talking, dazed and distracted to see his wife burst out weeping. Two large tears slowly rolled from the corners of her eyes to the corners of her mouth; he gasped, "Why, what's the matter? What's the trouble?"

By sheer will power she overcame her outburst and

answered in a calm voice while wiping the tears from her wet cheeks:

"Oh, nothing. Only I don't have an evening dress and therefore I can't go to that affair. Give the card to some friend at the office whose wife can dress better than I can."

He was stunned. He resumed, "Let's see, Mathilde. How much would a suitable outfit cost—one you could wear for other affairs too—something very simple?"

She thought it over for several seconds, going over her allowance and thinking also of the amount she could ask for without bringing an immediate refusal and an exclamation of dismay from the thrifty clerk.

Finally, she answered hesitatingly, "I'm not sure exactly, but I think with four hundred francs I could manage it."

He turned a bit pale, for he had set aside just that amount to buy a rifle so that, the following summer, he could join some friends who were getting up a group to shoot larks on the plain near Nanterre.

However, he said, "All right. I'll give you four hundred francs. But try to get a nice dress."

As the day of the party approached, Mme. Loisel seemed sad, moody, and ill at ease. Her outfit was ready, however. Her husband said to her one evening, "What's the matter? You've been all out of sorts for three days."

And she answered, "It's embarrassing not to have a jewel or a gem—nothing to wear on my dress. I'll look like a pauper: I'd almost rather not go to that party."

He answered, "Why not wear some flowers? They're very fashionable this season. For ten francs you can get two or three gorgeous roses."

She wasn't at all convinced. "No....There's nothing more humiliating than to look poor among a lot of rich women."

But her husband exclaimed, "My, but you're silly! Go see your friend Mme. Forestier and ask her to lend you some jewelry. You and she know each other well enough for you to do that."

She gave a cry of joy, "Why, that's so! I hadn't thought of it."

The next day she paid her friend a visit and told her of her predicament.

Mme Forestier went toward a large closet with mirrored doors, took out a large jewel box, brought it over, opened it, and said to Mme. Loisel: "Pick something out, my dear."

At first her eyes noted some bracelets, then a pearl necklace, then a Venetian cross, gold and gems, of marvelous workmanship. She tried on these adornments in front of the mirror, but hesitated, unable to decide which to part with and put back. She kept on asking, "Haven't you something else?"

"Oh, yes, keep on looking. I don't know just what you'd like."

All at once she found, in a black satin box, a superb diamond necklace; and her pulse beat faster with longing. Her hands trembled as she took it up. Clasping it around her throat, outside her high-necked dress, she stood in ecstasy looking at her reflection.

Then she asked, hesitatingly, pleading, "Could I borrow that, just that and nothing else?"

"Why, of course."

She threw her arms around her friend, kissed her warmly, and fled with her treasure.

The day of the party arrived. Mme. Loisel was a sensation. She was the prettiest one there, fashionable, gracious, smiling, and wild with joy. All the men turned to look at her, asked who she was, begged to be introduced. All the Cabinet officials wanted to waltz with her. The minister took notice of her.

She danced madly, wildly, drunk with pleasure, giving no thought to anything in the triumph of her beauty, the pride of her success, in a kind of happy cloud composed of all the adulation, of all the admiring glances, of all the awakened longings, of a sense of complete victory that is so sweet to a woman's heart.

She left around four o'clock in the morning. Her husband, since midnight, had been dozing in a small empty sitting room with three other gentlemen whose wives were having too good a time.

He threw over her shoulders the wraps he had brought for going home, modest garments of everyday life whose shabbiness clashed with the stylishness of her evening clothes. She felt this and longed to escape, unseen by the other women who were draped in expensive furs.

Loisel held her back.

"Hold on! You'll catch cold outside. I'll call a cab."

But she wouldn't listen to him and went rapidly down the stairs. When they were on the street, they didn't find a carriage; and they set out to hunt for one, hailing drivers whom they saw going by at a distance.

They walked toward the Seine, disconsolate and shivering. Finally on the docks they found one of those carriages that one sees in Paris only after nightfall, as if they were ashamed to show their drabness during daylight hours.

It dropped them at their door in the Rue des Martyrs, and they climbed wearily up to their apartment. For her, it was all over. For him, there was the thought that he would have to be at the Ministry at ten o'clock.

Before the mirror, she let the wraps fall from her

shoulders to see herself once again in all her glory. Suddenly she gave a cry. The necklace was gone.

Her husband, already half undressed, said, "What's the trouble?"

She turned toward him despairingly, "I . . . I . . . I don't have Mme. Forestier's necklace!"

"What! You can't mean it! It's impossible!"

They hunted everywhere, through the folds of the dress, through the folds of the coat, in the pockets. They found nothing.

He asked, "Are you sure you had it when leaving the dance?"

"Yes, I felt it when I was in the hall of the Ministry."

"But if you had lost it on the street we'd have heard it drop. It must be in the cab."

"Yes, Quite likely. Did you get its number?"

"No. Didn't you notice it either?"

"No."

They looked at each other aghast. Finally Loisel got dressed again.

"I'll retrace our steps on foot," he said, "to see if I can find it."

And he went out. She remained in her evening clothes, without the strength to go to bed, slumped in a chair in the unheated room, her mind a blank.

Her husband came in about seven o'clock. He had had no luck.

He went to the police station, to the newspapers to post a reward, to the cab companies, everywhere the slightest hope drove him.

That evening Loisel returned, pale, his face lined; still he had learned nothing.

"We'll have to write your friend," he said, "to tell her

you have broken the catch and are having it repaired. That will give us a little time to turn around."

She wrote to his dictation.

At the end of the week, they had given up all hope.

And Loisel, looking five years older, declared, "We must take steps to replace that piece of jewelry."

The next day they took the case to the jeweler whose name they found inside. He consulted his records. "I didn't sell that necklace, madame," he said. "I only supplied the case."

Then they went from one jeweler to another hunting for a similar necklace, going over their recollections, both sick with despair and anxiety.

They found, in a shop in Palais Royal, a string of diamonds which seemed exactly like the one they were seeking. It was priced at forty thousand francs. They could get it for thirty-six.

They asked the jeweler to hold it for them for three days. And they reached an agreement that he would take it back for thirty-four thousand if the lost one was found before the end of February.

Loisel had eighteen thousand francs he had inherited from his father. He would borrow the rest.

He went about raising the money, asking a thousand francs from one, four hundred from another, a hundred here, sixty there. He signed notes, made ruinous deals, did business with loan sharks, ran the whole gamut of moneylenders. He compromised the rest of his life, risked his signature without knowing if he'd be able to honor it, and then, terrified by the outlook for the future, by the blackness of despair about to close around him, by the propect of all the privations of the body and tortures of the spirit, he went to claim the new necklace with the thirty-six thousand francs which he placed on the counter of the shopkeeper.

When Mme. Loisel took the necklace back, Mme. Forestier said to her frostily, "You should have brought it back sooner; I might have needed it."

She didn't open the case, an action her friend was afraid of. If she had noticed the substitution, what would she have thought? What would she have said? Would she have thought her a thief?"

Mme. Loisel experienced the horrible life the needy live. She played her part, however, with sudden heroism. That frightful debt had to be paid. She would pay it. She dismissed her maid; they rented a garret under the eaves.

She learned to do the heavy housework, to perform the hateful duties of cooking. She washed dishes, wearing down her shell-pink nails scouring the grease from pots and pans; she scrubbed dirty linen, shirts, and cleaning rags which she hung on a line to dry; she took the garbage down to the street each morning and brought up water, stopping on each landing to get her breath. And, clad like a peasant woman, basket on arm, guarding sou by sou her scanty allowance, she bargained with the fruit dealers, the grocer, the butcher, and was insulted by them.

Each month notes had to be paid, and others renewed to give more time.

Her husband labored evenings to balance a tradesman's accounts, and at night, often, he copied documents at five sous a page.

And this went on for ten years.

Finally, all was paid back, everything including the exorbitant rates of the loan sharks and accumulated compound interest.

Mme. Loisel appeared an old woman, now. She became heavy, rough, harsh, like one of the poor. Her hair untended, her skirts askew, her hands red, her voice shrill, she even slopped water on her floors and scrubbed them herself. But, sometimes, while her husband was at work, she would sit near the window and think of that long-ago evening when, at the dance, she had been so beautiful and admired.

What would have happened if she had not lost that necklace? Who knows? Who can say? How strange and unpredictable life is! How little there is between happiness and misery!

Then one Sunday when she had gone for a walk on the Champs Élysées to relax a bit from the week's labors, she suddenly noticed a woman strolling with a child. It was Mme. Forestier, still young-looking; still beautiful, still charming.

Mme. Loisel felt a rush of emotion. Should she speak to her? Of course. And now that everything was paid off, she would tell her the whole story. Why not?

She went toward her. "Hello, Jeanne."

The other, not recognizing her, showed astonishment at being spoken to so familiarly by this common person. She stammered, "But . . . madame . . . I don't recognize . . . You must be mistaken."

"No, I'm Mathilde Loisel."

Her friend gave a cry, "Oh, my poor Mathilde, how you've changed!"

"Yes, I've had a hard time since last seeing you. And plenty of misfortunes—and all on account of you!"

"Of me . . . How do you mean?"

"Do you remember that diamond necklace you loaned me to wear to the dance at the Ministry?"

"Yes, but what about it?"

"Well, I lost it."

"You lost it! But you returned it."

"I brought you another just like it. And we've been paying for it for ten years now. You can imagine that wasn't easy for us who had nothing. Well, it's over now, and I am glad of it."

Mme. Forestier stopped short. "You mean to say you bought a diamond necklace to replace mine?"

"Yes. You never noticed, then? They were quite alike."

And she smiled with proud and simple joy.

Mme. Forestier, quite overcome, clasped her by the hands. "Oh, my poor Mathilde. But mine was only paste. Why, at most it was worth only five hundred francs!"

The
GOVERNESS

From the play *The Good Doctor*
by Neil Simon

MISTRESS. Julia! *(Calls again)* Julia!

[A young governess, Julia, comes rushing in. She stops before the desk and curtsies.]

JULIA *(head down)*. Yes, madame?

MISTRESS. Look at me, child. Pick your head up. I like to see your eyes when I speak to you.

JULIA *(lifts her head up)*. Yes, madame. *(But her head has a habit of slowly drifting down again.)*

MISTRESS. And how are the children coming along with their French lessons?

JULIA. They're very bright children, madame.

MISTRESS. Eyes up . . . They're bright, you say. Well, why not? And mathematics? They're doing well in mathematics, I assume?

JULIA. Yes, madame. Especially Vanya.

MISTRESS. Certainly. I knew it. I excelled in mathematics. He gets that from his mother, wouldn't you say?

JULIA. Yes, madame.

MISTRESS. Head up . . . *(She lifts head up.)* That's it. Don't be afraid to look people in the eyes, my dear. If you think of yourself as inferior, that's exactly how people will treat you.

JULIA. Yes, ma'am.

MISTRESS. A quiet girl, aren't you? . . . Now then, let's settle our accounts. I imagine you must need money although you never ask me for it yourself. Let's see now, we agreed on thirty rubles[1] a month, did we not?

JULIA *(surprised).* Forty, ma'am.

MISTRESS. No, no, thirty. I made a note of it. *(Points to the book)* I always pay my governesses thirty . . . Who told you forty?

JULIA. You did, ma'am. I spoke to no one else concerning money . . .

MISTRESS. Impossible. Maybe you *thought* you heard forty when I said thirty. If you kept your head up, that would never happen. Look at me again and I'll say it clearly. *Thirty rubles a month.*

JULIA. If you say so, ma'am.

MISTRESS. Settled. Thirty a month it is . . . Now then, you've been here two months exactly.

JULIA. Two months and five days.

MISTRESS. No, no. Exactly two months. I made a note of it. You should keep books the way I do so there wouldn't be these discrepancies.[2] So—we have two

---

1 **rubles** (rōō´bəlz): The ruble is the Russian unit of money, like the dollar in the United States.

2 **discrepancies** (dĭs-krĕp´ən-sēz): disagreements.

months at thirty rubles a month . . . comes to sixty rubles. Correct?

JULIA *(curtsies)*. Yes, ma'am. Thank you, ma'am.

MISTRESS. Subtract nine Sundays . . . We did agree to subtract Sundays, didn't we?

JULIA. No, ma'am.

MISTRESS. Eyes! Eyes! . . . Certainly we did. I've always subtracted Sundays. I didn't bother making a note of it because I always do it. Don't you recall when I said we will subtract Sundays?

JULIA. No, ma'am.

MISTRESS. Think.

JULIA *(thinks)*. No, ma'am.

MISTRESS. You weren't thinking. Your eyes were wandering. Look straight at my face and look hard . . . Do you remember now?

JULIA *(softly)*. Yes, ma'am.

MISTRESS. I didn't hear you, Julia.

JULIA *(louder)*. Yes, ma'am.

MISTRESS. Good. I was sure you'd remember . . . Plus three holidays. Correct?

JULIA. Two, ma'am. Christmas and New Year's.

MISTRESS. And your birthday. That's three.

JULIA. I worked on my birthday, ma'am.

MISTRESS. You did? There was no need to. My governesses never worked on their birthdays . . .

JULIA. But I did work, ma'am.

MISTRESS. But that's not the question, Julia. We're discussing financial matters now. I will, however, only count two holidays if you insist . . . Do you insist?

JULIA. I did work, ma'am.

MISTRESS. Then you *do* insist.

JULIA. No, ma'am.

MISTRESS. Very well. That's three holidays; therefore we take off twelve rubles. Now then, four days little Kolya was sick, and there were no lessons.

JULIA. But I gave lessons to Vanya.

MISTRESS. True. But I engaged you to teach two children, not one. Shall I pay you in full for doing only half the work?

JULIA. No, ma'am.

MISTRESS. So we'll deduct it . . . Now, three days you had a toothache and my husband gave you permission not to work after lunch. Correct?

JULIA. After four. I worked until four.

MISTRESS *(looks in the book)*. I have here. "Did not work after lunch." We have lunch at one and are finished at two, not at four, correct?

JULIA. Yes, ma'am. But I—

MISTRESS. That's another seven rubles . . . Seven and twelve is nineteen . . . Subtract . . . that leaves . . . forty-one rubles . . . Correct?

JULIA. Yes, ma'am. Thank you, ma'am.

MISTRESS. Now then, on January fourth you broke a teacup and saucer, is that true?

JULIA. Just the saucer, ma'am.

MISTRESS. What good is a teacup without a saucer, eh? . . . That's two rubles. The saucer was an heirloom. It cost much more, but let it go. I'm used to taking losses.

JULIA. Thank you, ma'am.

MISTRESS. Now then, January ninth, Kolya climbed a tree and tore his jacket.

JULIA. I forbad him to do so, ma'am.

MISTRESS. But he didn't listen, did he? . . . Ten rubles . . . January fourteenth, Vanya's shoes were stolen . . .

JULIA. By the maid, ma'am. You discharged her yourself.

MISTRESS. But you get paid good money to watch everything. I explained that in our first meeting. Perhaps you weren't listening. Were you listening that day, Julia, or was your head in the clouds?

JULIA. Yes, ma'am.

MISTRESS. Yes, your head was in the clouds?

JULIA. No, ma'am. I was listening.

MISTRESS. Good girl. So that means another five rubles off. *(Looks in the book)* . . . Ah yes . . . the sixteenth of January I gave you ten rubles.

JULIA. You didn't.

MISTRESS. But I made a note of it. Why would I make a note of it if I didn't give it to you?

JULIA. I don't know, ma'am.

MISTRESS. That's not a satisfactory answer, Julia . . . Why would I make a note of giving you ten rubles if I did not in fact give it to you, eh? . . . No answer? . . . Then I must have given it to you, mustn't I?

JULIA. Yes, ma'am. If you say so, ma'am.

MISTRESS. Well, certainly I say so. That's the point of this little talk. To clear these matters up . . . Take twenty-seven from forty-one, that leaves . . . fourteen, correct?

JULIA. Yes, ma'am. *(She turns away, softly crying.)*

MISTRESS. What's this? Tears? Are you crying? Has something made you unhappy, Julia? Please tell me. It pains me to see you like this. I'm so sensitive to tears. What is it?

JULIA. Only once since I've been here have I ever been given any money and that was by your husband. On my birthday he gave me three rubles.

MISTRESS. Really? There's no note of it in my book. I'll put it down now. *(She writes in the book.)* Three rubles. Thank you for telling me. Sometimes I'm a little lax with my accounts . . . Always shortchanging myself. So then, we take three more from fourteen . . . leaves eleven . . . Do you wish to check my figures?

JULIA. There's no need to, ma'am.

MISTRESS. Then we're all settled. Here's your salary for two months, dear. Eleven rubles. *(She puts the pile of coins on the desk.)* Count it.

JULIA. It's not necessary, ma'am.

MISTRESS. Come, come. Let's keep the records straight. Count it.

JULIA *(reluctantly counts it)*. One, two, three, four, five, six, seven, eight, nine, ten . . . ? There's only ten, ma'am.

MISTRESS. Are you sure? Possibly you dropped one . . . Look on the floor; see if there's a coin there.

JULIA. I didn't drop any, ma'am. I'm quite sure.

MISTRESS. Well, it's not here on my desk and I *know* I gave you eleven rubles. Look on the floor.

JULIA. It's all right, ma'am. Ten rubles will be fine.

MISTRESS. Well, keep the ten for now. And if we don't find it on the floor later, we'll discuss it again next month.

JULIA. Yes, ma'am. Thank you, ma'am. You're very kind, ma'am. *(She curtsies and then starts to leave.)*

MISTRESS. Julia! *(Julia stops, turns.)* Come back here. *(She crosses back to the desk and curtsies again.)* Why did you thank me?

JULIA. For the money, ma'am.

MISTRESS. For the money? . . . But don't you realize what I've done? I've cheated you . . . *Robbed* you! I have no such notes in my book. I made up whatever came into my mind. Instead of the eighty rubles which I

owe you, I gave you only ten. I have actually stolen
from you and still you thank me . . . Why?

JULIA. In the other places that I've worked, they didn't
give me anything at all.

MISTRESS. Then they cheated you even worse than I did . . .
I was playing a little joke on you. A cruel lesson just
to teach you. You're much too trusting, and in this
world that's very dangerous . . . I'm going to give you
the entire eighty rubles. *(Hands her an envelope)* It's
all ready for you. The rest is in this envelope. Here,
take it.

JULIA. As you wish, ma'am. *(She curtsies and starts to go
again.)*

MISTRESS. Julia! *(Julia stops.)* Is it possible to be so spine-
less? Why don't you protest? Why don't you speak
up? Why don't you cry out against this cruel and
unjust treatment? Is it really possible to be so guileless,[3] so innocent, such a—pardon me for being so
blunt—such a simpleton?

JULIA *(the faintest trace of a smile on her lips).* Yes,
ma'am . . . it's possible.

*[She curtsies again and runs off. The Mistress looks
after her a moment, a look of complete bafflement on
her face. The lights fade.]*

---

3 **guileless** (gīl´lĭs): simple; without deceit.

BEING ALIVE

A short story from the book
Heartbeats and Other Stories
by Peter D. Sieruta

Every Tuesday and Thursday afternoon the kid they called Kenny Wheels would come to watch our aerobics class. He'd sit against the wall, his face broken in half by a big smile, his fists banging double-time on the tray in front of him. Some people said he came just to watch the girls. It didn't matter to me; I wasn't particularly shy. And in a gym filled with girls in size-two pink, yellow, and orange leotards, I doubted he was paying much attention to a size twelve in a navy-blue sweatsuit like me. Besides, I was too busy with my own huffing and puffing to watch Kenny Wells in his wheelchair.

Until the day Kenny was kicked out of the gym.

Ms. Blair had just told us to pick up our jump ropes for the "aeropics" segment of the workout. A home-ec teacher by day, an exercise fiend by night, Ms. Blair was only a few years older than us seniors—but considered

very sophisticated because she was rumored to have a
live-in boyfriend. She claimed to have invented aeropics,
and all the girls were so hung up on her that nobody
questioned it. All I knew was that it was the hardest part
of the workout, and the only reason I persisted at it was
to burn up enough calories to justify buying a Moon Pie
or pack of Twinkies on the way home without feeling
guilty.

The music Ms. Blair played for the rope segment was
especially irritating. It started off nice and slow, hop and
pause and hop and pause, but steadily accelerated to hop-
hop-hop-hop-hop. By the time the song ended, most of
the girls were on the floor, gasping. That particular day,
two girls didn't stop jumping when the song ended: Kathi
Weiss and Addie Haines. All through school Kathi had
three things working for her: She was very pretty, very
athletic, and had a name ending with i. Addie was also
pretty and could run like the wind, but she had so much
pride that if you threw a fifty-dollar bill at her feet, she
wouldn't stoop to pick it up. It probably had something
to do with the fact she was the only black girl at our
entire high school.

Addie and Kathi were longtime rivals. For three years
Addie had beaten Kathi in the girls' division of our
school's 3-K Funrun. There was always some type of
competition going on between them. That afternoon they
continued jumping rope, facing each other, going faster
and faster, until I wasn't sure their feet were even hitting
the floor. Everyone was cheering, urging them on. When
Kathi finally fell out of rhythm and tumbled to the floor,
everyone laughed. Everyone including Kenny, whose
laugh was loud and wheezy. Addie was too proud to even
crack a smile over her victory; she just reached out a hand

to help Kathi get up. But Kathi got up on her own, her face red and sweaty. She listened to the laughter, then whirled at Kenny. "Stop that!" she shrieked. "Stop that horrible laughing!"

He tried to stop, but the laugh kept burbling out of his chest.

"What are you doing here anyway?" Kathi shouted. "This class is for *girls only!* Ms. Blair, make him leave! He's disrupting . . . everything!"

"Oh, Kathi . . ." Ms. Blair began, then shrugged.

"I mean it! I mean it!" Kathi shouted, stamping her foot. I remembered Kathi's eleventh-birthday party when she threw the same kind of tantrum because she didn't win at pin the tail on the donkey.

Ms. Blair shrugged again, twisting the chains at her neck. "Well, maybe you're right, Kathi. I guess we should be a little more businesslike in this class. Maybe we shouldn't allow visitors. Kenny—"

But she didn't have to finish the sentence, because he was already rolling toward the door with his head down, the thumb of his right hand controlling the button on his electric wheelchair.

When Addie followed him across the gym, I thought she was just going to help him with the door. But she followed him right through it. "Addie? Addie, where are you going?" Ms. Blair called.

She came back and stood in the doorway, her thin brown arms folded across the front of her blue leotard. "I don't like discrimination, Ms. Blair. If we're not allowing people with handicaps in the gym today, I'm going outside to run the track."

"Discrimination? Handicaps? Addie, I'm not asking Kenny to leave because of—I'm asking him to leave because he's a boy, and this is an all-girls class."

Addie never looked away from Ms. Blair. "You didn't say anything when Mel Jacobs and the guys from the football team came in last week."

"But—"

"I don't want to hear any *buts!*" Addie Haines was the only person in the whole school who could get away with that kind of talk. "Okay, boys in wheelchairs aren't allowed today. Next week it might be black girls." She pointed to herself. "Or girls with blond hair." She pointed at Kathi. "Girls with sweatsuits." She pointed at me.

Then she walked out.

An hour later, when I left the gym, Addie was still running the outdoor track. She wasn't the only one out there, but she was definitely the fastest. I didn't realize Kenny was sitting under a tree until I heard him calling out, "Go! Go! Go!"

I said, "Kenny, I'm sorry about what happened in there."

He was leaning forward in his chair, following Addie's progress with his eyes. He shrugged. "Blair says—she invented—that aeropicise. What a liar." As always, he spoke with a lot of difficulty, twisting his head as if he were biting the words out of the air.

"Blair's a bitch," I said.

He laughed and clapped his hands over his mouth. His hands reminded me of lobster claws. The fingers on each hand all seemed to be glued together; his thumbs moved independently.

Addie raced by and raised a hand in greeting. "Go! Go! Go!" yelled Kenny.

"You like sports, huh?"

"Watching. Not really—participating," he said. He

was a little guy, but for some reason he had a large, round face, and when he smiled—like he did at that moment— he looked like a happy jack-o'-lantern. "Aerobics," he said. "This is—my—aerobics." He lifted his hand and bent his thumb up and down several times. "Whew. Tired." He wiped imaginary sweat from his forehead with the side of his arm.

Addie ran off the track and sat down on the grass. "How's that?" she asked Kenny.

"Super!"

"Listen, Addie," I said, touching her arm. She leaned forward to tie her shoe—her way of pulling away without making a big deal of it. "That was a neat thing you did. I wish I'd had the nerve to walk out like that."

"You could have," she said, then turned to Kenny: "Thanks for pacing me like that."

He smiled.

"It worked," she said. "I ought to hire you as my trainer for the Funrun."

"What's it—like?" he asked.

"Winning?"

"No. Running."

Resting her chin on her knee, Addie looked off at the track.

When she didn't answer, Kenny said, "I wonder— because I don't—run. Can't find—Adidas—to fit my— wheels."

Addie smiled, but continued staring off. Finally she said, "When you start off, it feels like God's hand is on your back, giving you that first push. And then you're alone. It feels like you're part of the air. You're running toward something . . ." Her voice trailed off and she shrugged. "When I'm running, it feels the way being alive *should* feel." She looked at Kenny and added, "At least, it does for me."

She immediately got up and began doing stretching exercises. Maybe she was a little embarrassed. But I wasn't. Because when she talked about running, for a moment I felt like I could run too. Kenny must have felt the same way, because he said, "I—want to feel it."

She was bent over, her right hand holding her left foot. She stayed that way for a moment. "Feel what, Kenny?"

"Like I'm part of the air."

"Okay," she said. "Let's go for a run."

She moved behind his chair and grasped the handles, but when she tried pushing, the wheels only moved a few feet. "How much does this thing weigh?"

"A lot," he said. "My chair—weighs—more than— I do."

I remembered back to when I was a sophomore and Kenny had just started attending our school. He used to wheel himself around on a nonmotorized chair. "Didn't you have another chair?" I said. "Before you got this one?"

"Antique," he said. "From when—I could use—my hands a lot."

"That would be easier to push," I said.

Addie said, "I'll tell you what, Kenny. Some night we'll come to the track with your other chair. I'll take you for a ride so fast your wheels will spark."

He bounced up in his seat. "Tonight?"

"Where are you going, Nancy?" my younger sister asked that evening. My sister was a Kathi-Weiss-in-train-ing, resembling Kathi in everything from her clothes and hairstyle to her stubborn refusal to call me "Nance." Nance was plain. It was me: Nance Sherman. Nancy sounded too much like Micki, Muffy, Buffy, and all the other names the girls at our school were called.

"Out," I said, letting her draw her own conclusions.

"With a *boy*?"

"Maybe," I said, and left for the school yard.

Kenny's mother was to drop him at the high school at six thirty P.M. No one had invited me to join them, but I went anyway. I guess I just wanted to see how Kenny enjoyed "running."

"Nance! Kenny shouted, waving a claw in my direction.

Addie didn't seem surprised to see me. She was bent over, attaching Kenny's belt to the back of the wheelchair. Then she straightened and pushed the chair over to the track. No one else was running, but the big floodlights were still turned on because the football team had just finished practicing. The light caught Addie in profile, making her look like a proud African princess. "How fast—will we be—running?" Kenny asked.

"Like the wind," said Addie, and took off.

The light danced over and through the wheels, making Spirograph designs on the track. Feet pounded and wheels whirred, and then I heard it: Kenny's voice yelling, "Wheee!" His excitement pushed Kenny's voice into the upper register. It was the most amazing sound I'd ever heard. And that word! I couldn't remember saying "Wheee!" even as a child, but to hear a sixteen-year-old boy shout it just about broke my heart.

As they came around the last corner, facing me, I could see Kenny's face was completely split by that huge grin. Addie's breath was coming in little puffs of vapor, but—as always—she looked cool and aloof. I thought they'd pull over when they made a complete circle, but Addie kept going, around and around the track until something strange happened. The lights were set to go off automatically at seven o'clock, and when they did, the track went pitch dark. I couldn't see them at all, but I could hear the wheels, the feet, the breathing, the "Wheee!" and suddenly I felt I was there with them, running through the dark. First I felt I was Kenny being propelled through the night; then I was Addie, pounding the ground and pushing the chair in front of me. And then I was part of the air. It lasted only a second—that feeling— but when Addie and Kenny finally came off the track, I felt as high as if I'd been running too. My heart was beating fast, I was taking deep gulps of air.

I could hear Kenny bouncing around in his chair, saying, "Super! Super! Super!"

In the dark we sat and talked. I asked Addie what made her start running. "What made me start breathing?" she replied. "I've always run, but I didn't get into competition until I got to this school. I guess I got tired of being an outcast."

"You're not an outcast!" I said, thinking cliques and social circles were the last thing Addie seemed interested in; she always seemed above that sort of thing. "Now if you want to talk about outcasts, let's talk about *me*. I've never fit into anything in my life—including my Levi's."

Addie said, "I started entering the races to show them that I may act like an outcast and look like an outcast, but, hey, I've got it!"

"It?" said Kenny.

"It!" she said. "Whatever it takes to beat them. I'm showing them it's okay to be different."

"Outcasts, outcasts," said Kenny. "Am I the—only one here—who's always been an—average, normal guy?"

I wasn't sure how to take that until he started laughing. Then I laughed too. Addie's laugh was soft and low. I'd never heard her laugh before.

Kenny turned to me. "Don't you—run, Nance?"

"Only after Good Humor trucks," I said. "I mean, can you see this body in a race?"

"Why not?" said Addie.

"My sister calls me the Sherman tank," I said.

"I wish—I could run," said Kenny.

"You just did," said Addie.

"In a race," he said. "Run—in a race."

There was a long moment of silence. Then she said: "You can. You can run in a race. With me." It was too dark to see the expression on Addie's face. But I've always wondered what she looked like when she said those words.

The next day I approached her at school. "You aren't serious about running with Kenny in the Funrun."

"I am."

"Don't get me wrong," I said, "It's nice and all that, but it also means you're going to *lose*."

"Winning doesn't make that much difference to me," she said. "Running does."

"But, Addie, they do have sports events for the handicapped. Maybe he could get into that sometime."

"No," she said forcefully. "He wants to feel like everyone else at this school, and I'm going to help him do it."

I said, "You don't have to run for him just because he can't."

"I'm not doing it *because he can't*," she said. "I'm doing it *because I can*."

"Because I can": That must have been Addie's motto. I remembered the first time I heard her say that, the year we were freshmen. Addie had just won her first Funrun, and Kathi—who had lost by fifty seconds—went up to congratulate her. She pressed her cheek against Addie's, but her eyes were burning with anger. Later, walking away from the awards stand, I heard Kathi say in her most patronizing voice, "Well, Addie, I guess you run because you're trying for a sports scholarship to college, right?"

Addie turned cold eyes upon her. "No. My father is a pediatrician, so I guess he can afford to send me just about anyplace I want to go." Kathi's mouth dropped open just a millimeter, and Addie stared at her. "Why do *you* run, Kathi?"

Kathi shrugged. "Because I'm good at it, I guess. Because I think I can win."

"Ah," said Addie, holding a long, dark finger in front of Kathi's nose. "You run because you want to win. I run because I can."

At the time I didn't understand what she meant—that she could run just for the joy of it. I knew how I'd feel if I ran: I'd want the awards. Even now I found it hard to believe Addie could pass up the chance to win.

I said, "But Addie, you're a senior. This will be your last chance for the Funrun. You won't be here next year."

She looked past me. "Kenny may not be here next year either."

"What do you mean? He's only a junior."

"I mean that I've been looking at some of my father's medical books," she said.

"I don't want to hear this," I said.

"Remember when he could talk more clearly than he does now? When he could wheel himself around in his chair? When he could move his fingers and take notes in class instead of carrying around that big tape recorder?"

"Don't tell me any more," I said, walking away.

I was always walking away from things I didn't want to hear. My father liked to tell about the time I was three years old and they brought my little sister home from the hospital. I hid under the bed, yelling, "Is it gone yet?" Maybe I hadn't changed much.

That night I ended up at the school yard. I knew I would. Again nobody had asked me to come.

Addie wheeled Kenny out to the track. "Keep your eye on the stopwatch," she told him.

"I can do that," I said.

"I'll keep you—going fast." He twisted his head around to look at her face. "I'll cheer—a lot."

"Sounds good," she said, and took off running.

"Go! Go! Go! Go!" I heard Kenny shout.

I watched the seconds tick around the stopwatch. When they came back, Addie said, "What was our time?"

I held up the watch, and she grimaced. "Well, usually I go about twice as fast as that," she muttered. "Let's try it again."

And that was how it went every night for the next three weeks. I'd leave the house—leaving my sister with the impression I was going on a date—and meet Addie and Kenny at the track. I'd hold the stopwatch as Addie ran and Kenny shouted encouragement. Sometimes I even felt like I was part of the air again.

Two nights before the race Addie ran the whole 3-K, just to make sure she could do it. She was wiped out when she got back, and their time wasn't that good. But it didn't seem to bother her. "We did it," she told Kenny. "We did run the whole three kilometers."

"We did it!" he shouted, and he looked happy, really happy.

Addie told us to meet her in front of the school at seven on Friday evening. For the first time she made a point of including me in the invitation. I thought she wanted me to time their last practice session, but when I got there, Addie was wearing a skirt instead of her usual leotard. "What's going on?" I asked. "Aren't you practicing tonight?"

"Not tonight," said Kenny.

Addie began pushing his chair down the sidewalk, and I ran to help her. "Where are we going?" I asked.

"Dinner," said Addie.

We walked the two blocks to a small restaurant I'd never noticed before. There were only a few people inside, all of them older than our parents. It was the type of restaurant most of the kids at our school would laugh at, but The Pasta Bowl—with its Italian songs on the jukebox and red plastic tablecloths—was my kind of place. People yelled their orders across the room and ran back and forth with trays of pizza and pitchers of beer.

I went to the counter for a pitcher of Coke, and when I returned, Addie was saying, "It's a good idea to load up on a lot of carbohydrates the night before a race. I usually eat spaghetti, but some people like pizza or pancakes."

"Oh, boy," said Kenny. "I want a—pizza."

"This is great," I said. "Next time my sister complains about my eating, I'm going to tell her I'm carbohydrate loading for a race."

Kenny tore open the end of his straw and blew the wrapper across the table at me; I shot mine back at him.

I realized it was the first time Addie, Kenny, and I had been together off the school track. All those nights we'd spent in training for the race were coming to an end. I didn't want to think about that. "Let's get a large pizza," I said.

Addie ordered a huge plate of spaghetti, and Kenny and I split the pizza. I sat there wolfing down my slices, and no one said, "Nancy, don't you think you've had enough?" or pushed salad at me. In fact, Addie offered me a taste of her spaghetti.

Kenny said, "Last year—when our homeroom won that prize—for best attendance—we had a pizza party." He paused to swipe at a strand of cheese hanging off his hand. "When I got my slice—Mrs. Pelton came over— and she wanted to—cut my pizza in small pieces."

"Why?" asked Addie.

"That's what I wonder," said Kenny. "She didn't want to cut—anyone else's."

I said, "That would make me really mad."

Kenny lowered his voice. "Pissed me off."

He reached forward with both hands and took another slice off the tray. "So when she was standing there beside my chair—I dropped my pizza. I dropped it right—on her skirt." He chewed for a few seconds, then added. "You know how sometimes—my hands don't work right." And he winked.

Addie and I burst out laughing, and Kenny joined in with his loud, wheezy laugh.

When it was time to leave, we all wanted to pay the check ourselves. Kenny took out his wallet and counted dollar bills while I tried to grab the check from Addie's hand. "No," said Addie. "I invited you two out."

"Okay," I said. "But next time I'm paying."

It wasn't until I was home in bed that I thought about what I'd said: "Next time." No one had ever said there'd be a next time.

The next morning I walked to the field in the early-morning cold. It was strange to see all the Kathis and Muffys and Phils and Chases of our town out on that track. For weeks it had been a private nighttime playground for Addie and Kenny and me.

When I finally found Addie and Kenny, they were in the middle of a confrontation with Kathi Weiss. "What do you think you're doing?" Kathi demanded.

"We're going to run," Addie replied calmly.

"Oh, no! Oh, no! You are *not* running with him."

"Try stopping us." said Addie.

"I just might! You better believe I just might! What is this, some hokey publicity stunt to get your name in the paper? Something to put on your college application?"

Kenny looked hurt for a second, and Addie moved in front of him—blocking Kathi from his view. "Listen, Weiss," she said. "Why don't you accept the fact that now you can win the girls' division—and just shut up."

Nobody ever told Kathi to shut up. She filled herself up with air to start yelling. But then a glimmer of understanding seemed to cross her face. She turned abruptly and walked away.

The race was almost ready to start. I only had time to say a quick "Good luck, you guys."

Addie smiled. Kenny stuck his thumb in the air.

"Runners, take your places," a voice boomed, and I ran off the track to stand in the crowd, never taking my eyes off them. His hands gripped the arms of the chair tightly. Her hands gripped the handles.

When the starting gun went off, seventy-two pairs of feet and one set of wheels went zipping across the line. The race course consisted of one lap around the track, then out onto the street for about a mile, and back to the track for another lap. Addie's legs were pumping like pistons, and the wheels of the chair spun so fast, I couldn't see the spokes. But by the time they had completed that first lap one thing was clear: They were going to lose.

Seeing Addie and Kenny about two thirds of the way behind the leaders, I knew there was no hope. Of course we'd known it all along, but I guess I still harbored some secret hope for a miracle. But now I could see Bob Beechum, Gary Rosen, and Perry Astor were shoulder to shoulder at the front of the pack. Of the girls, Kathi Weiss wasn't too far behind them. I had never seen so much concentration on her face.

When Addie and Kenny passed me and started out toward the street, neither of them looked in my direction. Addie was still pumping hard, and Kenny was yelling, "Go! Go! Go!"

I was used to Addie and Kenny's usual pace, where I could eat a big bag of Cheetos before they finished one kilometer. But this was different. It didn't seem all that long before the first runners were coming back into the field. I wondered how far behind my friends were. Perry Astor crossed the finish line, winning the boys' medal, and a few minutes later Kathi Weiss bounded across the line, tears of pain or exhaustion or happiness streaming down her face.

The announcer was calling off the finishes as each kid crossed the line. "Thirty-eight, thirty-nine, forty, forty-one."

And then I saw them coming back onto the track—
Addie kicking her feet into the air, puffing like an engine,
Kenny urging her on. When they finally crossed the finish line, Kenny's fists were raised in the air. They had
come in forty-fifth. Addie walked the chair to a slow
stop, then moved away as people gathered around
Kenny, shaking his hand, patting his back. Occasionally,
above their congratulations, I heard his voice: "Wow!
Super! Super!"

And I realized it didn't matter to Kenny whether they
came in first, forty-fifth, or seventy-second. He was
happy just to be part of it. I went looking for Addie and
found her standing near the stage, watching Kathi and
Perry receive their medals. Addie stood tall—as always—
and her head was held high—as always. But there was
something in her eyes I'd never seen before.

"Hi!" I shouted, moving toward her. My first impulse
was to hug Addie. But as I got closer, the look in her eyes
told me to back off.

"Congratulations!" I said, standing in front of her,
not sure what to do.

"Thanks," she said, then turned to watch the medal
presentation.

"You did great!"

"Nance, please! I'm trying to watch the presentation."

I saw a hand go up to her eye and realized she was
crying. Despite all her talk, winning *had* been important
to her. It was kind of ironic, considering it didn't matter
to Kenny at all. Then it hit me: The reason Addie had run
with Kenny was that no one else would. Anyone else
could have run with him—Kenny wouldn't have cared—
while Addie ran for the medal. I said to Addie, "I never
thought of this until now, but you should have been run-

ning. Someone else could have run with Kenny. *I could have tried.*"

"Yes," she said coldly. "You *could* have."

For the next twenty-four hours I was miserable. I was furious at myself for being so dim-witted, so self-centered that I'd cost Addie her chance to win the race. I was furious at Addie for being such a hypocrite—saying she didn't care about winning when she really did. I was even mad at Kenny, because it seemed he was even more self-involved than I was. Didn't he realize Addie might have really wanted to run? Didn't he care that she was giving up her last chance just to give him a good time?

On Sunday evening I automatically put on my army jacket at six fifteen. I didn't realize I'd done it until my younger sister said, "Off to meet Mr. Right?" and I realized I'd been a hypocrite myself—deliberately trying to look good in my sister's eyes by inventing a boyfriend. I said, "I don't have a boyfriend. I never did. I'm going out to find my two friends, Addie Haines and Kenny Wells!"

Then I crashed out the door. Behind me, my sister was shouting, "Kenny *Wheels?* The *cripple?* And that *black* girl?"

Of course, the field was dark, but I could hear her pounding footsteps on the track. I had never heard her run that fast before; I realized that all those weeks of pushing Kenny's chair had strengthened her, increased her speed. She ran for a long, long time, even though I was sure she knew I was there. Finally she came running off the track with a stop-watch in her hand and sat down beside me.

Now if she would only talk to me.

She held up the stopwatch and said, "My own private

Funrun. I won. In fact, it was my best time ever." She didn't seem to be angry at me anymore.

I said, "Too bad I was the only one here to see it."

"Let's walk," she said, getting up.

We walked for a long time without talking. I think she was waiting for her breathing to level off before she spoke. Finally: "Yesterday was not one of my finer moments."

"Mine either," I admitted.

"I couldn't *believe* how bad it hurt to see Kathi Weiss with that medal around her neck. I couldn't *believe* how much I'd been lying to myself."

"I can't believe how dumb I've been," I said.

She continued, "I thought I was above that attitude, but I realized yesterday that I'm not. All yesterday and today I was down, down, down." Her voice dropped lower with each "down." "And then I thought to myself, Okay, Addie, so you're not perfect. You're petty and jealous and a hypocrite, so what? It's all part of being alive."

"I wish I could have that attitude," I began. "I can't stand myself."

"Neither can I sometimes," she admitted, and laughed.

We walked on in silence, heading for Kenny's house. We never said we were going there; we just did. And we ended up at the school a little while later, Addie on one side of the chair, me on the other, with Kenny between us, just taking a stroll down the track. Addie, Kenny, and me. Being alive.

the
LEAVING

A short story from the book *The Leaving*
by Budge Wilson

She took me with her the day she left. "Where y' goin',
Ma?" I asked. She was standing beside my bed with her
coat on.

"Away," said Ma. "And yer comin', too."

I didn't want to go anywhere. It was three o'clock in
the morning, and I was warm in my bed.

"Why me?" I complained.

I was too sleepy to think of any more complicated
questions. In any case, there were no choices and very few
questions back then when we were kids. You went to
school and you came home on the school bus. If your
father wanted you to shovel snow or fetch eggs, he told
you, and you did it. He didn't ask. He told. Same with Ma.
I did the dishes and brought in the firewood when it was
required. She just pointed to the sink or to the woodbox,
and I would leave whatever I was doing and start work.

But at 3:00 a.m., the situation seemed unusual enough to permit a question. Therefore I asked again, "Why me?"

"Because yer the smartest," she said. "And because yer a woman."

I was twelve years old that spring.

Ma was a tall, rangy woman. She had a strong handsome face, with high cheekbones and a good firm chin line. Her lips were full. Her teeth were her own, although she smiled so rarely that you seldom saw them; her mouth tended to be held in a set straight line. She did not exactly frown; it was more as though she were loosely clenching her teeth. Her eyes were veiled, as if she had shut herself off from her surroundings and was thinking either private thoughts or nothing at all. Oh, she was kind enough and gentle enough when we needed it, though perhaps we needed it more often than she knew. But when we had cut knees or tonsillectomies, or when friends broke our hearts, she would hold us and hug us. Her mouth would lose its hard tight shape, and her eyes would come alive with concern and love.

Her lovely crisp auburn hair was short and unshaped making her face look uncompromising and austere. She wore baggy slacks over her excellent legs, and she owned two shabby grey sweaters and two faded graceless blouses. I did not ask myself why my mother looked this way, or why she had retreated behind her frozen face. One accepts one's parents for a long time, without theory or question. Speculation comes later, with adolescence and all the uncertainty and confusion it brings.

But when she woke me that chilly May morning, I was still a child. I rose and dressed quickly, packing my school bag with my pyjamas and toothbrush, the book I was reading, a package of gum, the string of Woolworth pearls that my grandmother had given me on my tenth birthday, and some paper to write and draw on. I wore jeans, my favourite blue sweater, my winter jacket, and rubber boots. I forgot my hat.

My mother had told me to be quiet, so I slithered down the stairs without a single board creaking. She was waiting at the door, holding a black cardboard suitcase with a strap around it. A shopping bag held sandwiches and some of last fall's bruised apples. She wore a brown car coat over her black slacks, and her hair was hidden under a grey wool kerchief. Her mouth had its tense fixed look but her eyes were alive. Even at my age and at that hour, I could see that.

We stopped briefly before walking out into the cold night air. The stove in the kitchen was making chugging noises, and from different parts of the small house could be heard a variety of snores and heavy breathing. My four brothers and my father were not going to notice our departure.

For a moment, my mother seemed to hesitate. Her mouth softened, and a line deepened between her eyebrows. Then she straightened her shoulders and opened the door. "Move!" she whispered.

We stepped into the night and started walking down the mountain in the direction of town, six miles away. I did not quarrel with the need for this strange nocturnal journey, but I did question the reason.

"Ma," I said.

She turned and looked at me.

"Ma. Why are we leavin'?"

She didn't answer right away. It crossed my mind that she might not be sure of the reason herself. This was a frightening thought. But apparently she knew.

"I plans t' do some thinkin'," she said.

We walked quickly through the night. North and South Mountains closed off the sky behind us and far ahead, but a full moon made it easy to see our way on the frosty road. The hill country was full of scrub growth, stubby spruce, and sprawling alders, unlike the tidy fields and orchards of the Valley. But the frost lent a silver magic to the bushes and the rough ground, and the moonlight gave a still dignity to the shabby houses. It was cold, and I shivered. "Fergot yer hat," said Ma. "Here." She took the warm wool kerchief from her head and gave it to me. I took it. Parents were invincible, and presumably would not feel the cold. My mother was not a complainer. She was an endurer. It was 1969, and she was forty-five years old.

When we reached Annapolis, we stopped at a small house on the edge of town, and Ma put down her suitcase and dug around in her purse. She took out a key and opened the door. Even my silent mother seemed to think that an explanation was required. "Lida Johnson's in Glace Bay, visitin' her daughter. Said I could use the house while she's gone. Normie's at a 4-H meetin' in Bridgetown. Joseph's truckin'. We'll wait here till th' train goes."

"Maw," I asked, "how long we gonna be gone?"

She bent her head down from its rigid position and looked at the floorboards of the front hall. She touched her mouth briefly with her fist. She closed her eyes for a second and took a deep breath.

"Dunno," she replied. "Till it's time."

We slept in the parlour until we left for the station. I guess that six-mile walk had shunted me straight from childhood into adolescence, because I did an awful lot of thinking between Annapolis and Halifax. But at first I was too busy to think. I was on a train, and I had never been inside one before. There were things to investigate—the tiny washroom with its little sink, and the funny way to flush the toilet. In the main part of the Dayliner, the seats slid up and down so that people could sleep if they wanted to. I watched the world speed by the windows—men working on the roads; kids playing in the schoolyards; cows standing dumbly outside barns in the chilly air, all facing in the same direction; places and towns I had never seen till then. My ma looked over at me and placed a comic book and a bag of peanuts on my lap. "Fer th' trip," she said, and smiled, patting my knee in an unfamiliar gesture. "Mind missin' school?" she added.

"No," I said. But I did. I had a part in the class play, and there was a practice that afternoon. I was the chief fairy, and I had twenty-five lines, all of which I knew by heart already. But this trip was also a pretty special, if alarming, adventure. It had a beginning but no definite end, and we were still speeding toward the middle. What would Halifax be like? We never had enough money to have more than one ride on the Exhibition Ferris wheel at Lawrencetown; but here we were buying train tickets and reading comics and eating peanuts and travelling to heaven knows what expensive thrills.

"Maw," I asked, "where'd the money come from?"

She looked at me, troubled.

"Don't ask," she said. "I'll tell you when you're eighteen."

Eighteen! I might as well relax and enjoy myself. But I wondered.

Before long, she fell asleep, and I felt free to think.

Until then, it was almost as though I were afraid she would read my thoughts.

Why had we left? How long would we be gone? How would Pa and my brothers cook their dinner? How would they make their beds? Who would they complain to after a hard day? Who would fetch the eggs, the mail, the water, the wood, the groceries? Who would wash their overalls, mend their socks, put bandages on their cuts? It was inconceivable to me that they could survive for long without us.

When we reached Halifax, we went to what I now realize was a cheap and shabby hotel in the South End of the city. But to me it seemed the height of luxury. The bed was made of some kind of shiny yellow wood. The bedspread was an intense pink, with raised nubbles all over it. A stained spittoon sat in the corner. There was actually a sink in the room, with taps that offered both cold and hot water. A toilet that flushed was down the hall. I checked under the bed; there was no chamber pot. But who needed it? There were two pictures on the walls— one of a curly-headed blonde, displaying a lot of bare flesh, and another of three dead ducks hanging upside down from a nail. I spent a lot of time inspecting both of these pictures.

Halifax was a shock to me. How could the buildings be so huge and the stores so grand? Here I was in the province's capital city before I really understood what a capital city could be. I admired the old stone buildings with their carvings around the doors and windows. I stretched my neck to see the tops of the modern apartments, with their glass and concrete reaching up into the clouds. The buses and cars alarmed me as they rushed up and down the long streets, but they excited me, too. The weather changed; it was warm and comforting, and the wind was gentle and caressing. We went down the hill to the harbour, and saw the bridge; rooted in the ground and in the sea bottom, it lifted its enormous metal wings into the sky. I marvelled that a thing so strong could be so graceful, so beautiful. What a lovely way, I thought, to get from one place to another. We walked across the bridge to Dartmouth, and watched the ships, far below, headed for Europe, for Africa, for the distant North. My mother, who had started to talk, told me about all these things. It was as though she were trying to tell me something important, but didn't want to say things right out. "They're goin' somewheres," she said. Later on, she took me out to Dalhousie University, and we walked among the granite buildings and beside the playing fields. "If yer as smart as the teacher claims," she said, "maybe you'll come here some day t' learn." I thought this highly unlikely. If we couldn't afford running water, how could we afford such a thing as that? I said so.

"They's ways," she said.

We walked up and down Spring Garden Road and gazed in the big windows. I looked at a candy store with at least five million kinds of candy, shops with dresses so fancy that I could scarcely believe it, shelves full of diamonds and gold and sparkling crystal. "Is there ways for all this, too?" I asked my mother. She hesitated.

"Don't need all that stuff," she concluded.

The weather was dazzling—a sunny Nova Scotia May day.

We walked through the huge iron gates into the Public Gardens and ate our sandwiches and apples beside the duck pond. I kicked off my rubber boots and

wiggled my toes in the sun as I watched the swans and
the yellow ducklings. The Gardens were immense, full
of massive and intricate flowerbeds, winding paths, and
strange exotic trees. There were statues, a splashing
fountain, an elaborate round bandstand, and a little river
with a curved bridge over it. Lovers strolled arm in arm,
and children shrieked with laughter as they chased the
pigeons. I asked Ma why everyone seemed so happy.
"Dunno," she said. "Weather does things t' people."
She looked around. "And maybe some of them's free,"
she added.

On the second day, we watched women racing to
work in the morning, mini-skirts flipping, heels clicking,
faces eager, faces tense. We looked on as shopping women
pulled twenty-dollar bills out of their purses as though
they were nickels. We saw the drunks sleeping on the
pavement outside the mission. We visited the courthouse
and looked at the pictures of the stern-faced judges as
they watched us from the walls. "They fixes things what
aren't right," said Ma. I wondered how. "But not
always," she added.

We spent an hour in the public library, looking at the
shelves and shelves of books, smelling their wonderful
book smells, idly turning the pages. On a book dolly, she
picked up a copy of *The Feminine Mystique.* She, who
had not to my knowledge read a single book since I was
born, said shyly, "I read this book." I was astonished.

"You!" I exclaimed. "How come? When?"

"I kin read!" she retorted, miffed. "Even if y' leaves
school in grade 5, y' kin read. Y' reads slow, but y' knows
how."

"But where'd you get it?" I demanded, amazed.

"Y' remember that day the Salvation Army lady

brought us that big box o' clothes?" she asked. "Yer pa was mad and said we didn't need no charity. But I hid the box, and after a time he forgot about it. Well, there was other things in there, too—an egg beater, some toys what I gave to Lizzie's kids, even a string o' yellow beads and a bracelet that I bin savin' fer you. And some books. There was comic books and that big colourin' book y' got fer Christmas, and them *Popular Mechanics* magazines the boys read, and a coupla others. And this." She placed the palm of her hand on the book. "Seemed like it was for me, special. So I read it. She was real tough goin', but I read every word. Took me near a year. Finished it last Thursday."

I could hardly believe it. My ma didn't even read recipes. She kept them all in her head. I asked, "Was it good?"

She thought for a moment before answering. "She was a real troublin' book. But she was good."

I couldn't understand that. "If it was so troublin', why was it so good?"

She answered that one without hesitation. "Found I weren't alone," she said. She stroked its cover tenderly before putting it back on the dolly. I liked the library, with all the silent people bent over their books, and the librarians moving soundlessly to and fro. I wasn't used to quiet places.

In the afternoon, we climbed the Citadel and went into its museum, walking up and down among the sea things, old things, rich things. Later on, we went to what I thought was a very fancy restaurant. There were bright, shiny chrome tables with place mats of paper lace and green glass ashtrays. I ordered a hot dog and chips, because that was my favourite meal. My mother, her mouth now soft and cheerful, ordered something with a strange name.

"Ain't gonna come all this way and spend all th' hen money jest t' eat what I kin eat at home," she said.

The egg money! So that was it. I let on I didn't notice. But a thrill of fear ran through me. I wondered what Pa would do.

In the evening we returned early to the hotel, and I slept deeply, but with strange and troubled dreams.

On the third day, Ma said, "It's time. T'day we go home." I asked why.

"Because," she said.

"Because why?" I insisted.

She was silent for a moment, and then said again, "It's time." I was pleased. It had been an interesting trip, but it frightened me a little because there were no explanations, no answers to my unspoken questions. Besides, I was afraid that someone else would get to be chief fairy in the school play. "Have you done yer thinkin'?" I asked. She looked at me strangely. There was hope in her look and an odd fierce dignity.

"I has," she said.

We took the bus home instead of the train, and it was late afternoon when we arrived in Annapolis to start the six-mile climb to our farm. The day was damp and cold, and I wore my mother's wool kerchief again. We were very quiet, and I knew she was nervous. Her mouth was back in its taut line, and her eyes were troubled. But even in the wind, her shoulders were straight and firm, and I could feel a difference in her. Fearful though her eyes were, she was fully alert, and you could sense a new dogged strength in the set of her face.

There was no such strength in me, except such as I derived from her. Home is home when you are twelve, and I did not want to live a tourist's life in Halifax forever. But I worried every step of the six long miles.

As we turned the bend at Harrison's Corner, we could see the farm in the distance. It was as though I were seeing it for the first time. The house had been white once, but it had needed paint for almost nineteen years. Around the yard was a confusion of junk of all kinds: two discarded cars—lopsided and without wheels—an unpiled jumble of firewood, buckets, a broken hoe, rusty tools, an old oil drum for burning garbage. To the left were the few acres of untidy fields, dotted with spruce trees and the grey skeletons of trees long dead of Dutch elm disease. To the right, close to the henhouse, was the barn—small and unpainted, grey and shabby in the dim afternoon light. We could hear the two cows complaining, waiting for milking time.

When we opened the kitchen door, they were all there. My four big brothers were playing cards at the table, and my father was sitting by the kitchen stove, smoking a cigarette and drinking from a bottle of beer. I had forgotten how darkly handsome he was. But because it was not Sunday, he was unshaven, and his eyes glared out at us from beneath heavy black eyebrows.

Pa rose from his chair and faced us. He was very tall, and his head almost reached the low ceiling. He seemed to fill the entire room. He crushed out his cigarette on the top of the stove.

His voice was low and threatening. "Where you bin, woman?" he said.

She spoke, and I was amazed that she had the

courage. Then I realized with a jolt that his words were little different in tone and substance from hundreds I had heard before: "How come my supper's not ready, woman?" "Move smart, woman! I'm pressed fer time!" "Shut up them damn kids, woman!" "Move them buckets, woman! They're in my way!" "This food ain't fit t' eat, woman. Take it away!"

She spoke quietly and with dignity. "You is right to be angry, Lester," she said. "I left a note fer y', but I shoulda tole y' before I left."

"Shut yer mouth, woman, and git my supper!" he shouted, slamming the beer bottle down on the table.

She moved to the centre of the room and faced him. "My name," she began, and faltered. She cleared her throat and ran her tongue over her lower lip. "My name," she repeated, this time more steadily, "is Elizabeth."

He was dumbfounded. My brothers raised their heads from their card game and waited, cards poised in midair.

Pa looked at her. He looked at me. Then he looked at Jem and Daniel and Ira and Bernard, sitting there silent and still like four statues, waiting for his reaction.

Suddenly my father threw back his head and laughed. His ugly laughter filled the little kitchen, and we all listened, frozen, wishing for it to stop.

"'My name is Elizabeth!'" he mocked, between choking guffaws, slapping his thighs and holding his stomach, and then he repeated himself and her, mincingly, "'My . . . name . . . is . . . Elizabeth!'" Then his face changed, and there was silence. "Git over here 'n' make my supper, woman! I'm gonna milk them cows. But my belly is right empty, and y' better be ready when I gits back from th' chores!"

I watched my mother. During the laughter, I could see her retreat for a minute behind her eyes, expressionless, lifeless, beaten. Then she took a deep breath and looked at him directly, squarely, with no fear in her face. Pain, yes, but no fear. My brothers looked down and continued their card game.

"Act smart there, Sylvie," she said to me, as soon as he had left. "I need yer help bad. You clean up, 'n' I'll fix supper." She was already moving swiftly about the kitchen, fetching food, chopping onions, peeling potatoes.

In the sink was a mountainous pile of dirty dishes. Open cans, crusted with stale food, cluttered the counter. I surveyed the scene with distaste.

"Ma," I asked, complaining like the true adolescent that I had now become, "how come they couldna washed the dishes themselves? They goes huntin' and fishin' and has lotsa little vacations in th' winter. We always do their work for them when they're gone. How come we gotta clean up their mess?"

"Listen," she said, cutting the potatoes and dropping them into the hot fat, "the way I sees it is y' kin ask fer kindness or politeness from time t' time. But y' can't expect no miracles. It's my own fault fer raisin' four boys like they was little men. I shoulda put them in front of a dishpan fifteen years ago. Now it's too late. Yer pa's ma did the same thing. She aimed t' raise a boy who was strong and brave, with no soft edges." She wiped her forehead with the back of her hand "All along I bin blamin' men fer bein' men. But now I see that oftentimes it's the women that makes them that way." It was a long, long speech for my ma. But she went on. "The boys is seventeen, eighteen, nineteen and twenty years old. Y' can't start makin' 'em over now. They's set." Then she

smiled wryly, with a rare show of humour. She bowed
formally in the direction of the card game. "I apologizes,"
she said, "to your future wives."

Then she stopped, and looked from one son's face to
the next, and so on, around the table. "I loves you all,
regardless," she said softly, "and it's worth a try. Jem"—
she spoke to the youngest—"I'd be right grateful if you'd
fetch some water for Sylvie. She's real tired after the long
walk."

Jem looked at his brothers, and then he looked at her.
Water carrying was woman's work, and she knew she was
asking a lot of him. He rose silently, took the bucket from
her, and went outside to the well.

"And you," she said, addressing Daniel and Ira and
Bernard, "One snigger out of you, and yer in bad trouble." I'm sure she knew she was taking an awful chance.
You can say a thing like that to little boys, but these were
grown men. But no one moved or so much as smiled
when Jem returned. "I thank you right kindly," said Ma,
thereby delivering a speech as unusual as her other one.

You could say, I suppose, that our leaving made no
large difference in my mother's life. She still worked without pay or praise, and was often spoken to as though she
were without worth or attraction. Her days were long
and thankless. She emptied chamber pots and spittoons,
scrubbed overalls and sheets on her own mother's scrub
board, and peeled the frozen clothes from the line in winter with aching fingers. But not all things remained the
same. She now stood up to my father. Her old paralytic
fear was gone, and she was able to speak with remarkable
force and dignity. She did not nag. Nagging is like a con-
stant blow with a small blunt instrument. It annoys, but it

seldom makes more than a small dent. When she chose to object to Pa's cruel or unfair behaviour, her instrument was a shining steel knife with a polished cutting edge. A weapon like that seemed to make my father realize that if he went too far—if he beat her, or if he scolded too often or too unjustly—she would leave. After all, she had done it once before. And this time, she might not return.

So there were changes. One day, for no apparent reason, he started to call her Elizabeth. She did not let on that this was remarkable, but the tight line of her mouth relaxed, and she made him a lemon pie for supper. She fixed up the attic storeroom as a workroom for herself. The boys lugged up her treadle sewing machine, and she brought in an old wicker chair and a table from the barn. It was a hot room in summer and cold in winter, but it was her own place—her escape. She made curtains from material bought at Frenchy's, and hooked a little rug for the floor. No one was allowed to go there except her. She always emerged from this room softer, gentler, more still.

I never did hear a single word about the missing egg money. Maybe Pa didn't notice, or perhaps Ma attacked the subject with her sharp-edged knife. Possibly it was the egg money that sent me to Dalhousie—that and my scholarship and my summer jobs. I never asked. I didn't really want to know.

When I was home last February during the term break, I stole a look into Ma's attic room. There were library books on the table, material on the sewing machine, paper piled on the floor for her letters to me and to the boys. I respected her privacy and did not go in. But the room, even in that chilly winter attic, looked like an inviting place.

My ma is now fifty-five, and has a lot of life still to

live. My pa is fifty-eight. He still shaves once a week, and he has not yet cleared up the yard. But he often speaks to my mother as though she were more of a person and less of a thing. Sometimes he says thank-you. He still has a raging temper, but he is an old dog, and new tricks come hard. He loves my mother and she him, with a kind of love that is difficult for my generation to understand or define. In another time and in another place, the changes could have been more marked. But my mother is a tough and patient woman, and these differences seem to be enough for her. Her hair is worn less severely. Her mouth is not set so straight and cold and firm. She talks more. She has made a pretty yellow blouse to wear with her baggy slacks. She smiles often, and she is teaching her two grandsons how to wash dishes and make cookies.

≈

I often wonder about these things: but when my mind approaches the reasons for all that has happened, my thinking slides away and my vision blurs. Certainly the book and the leaving do not explain everything. Maybe my mother was ready to move into and out of herself anyway; and no one can know exactly what went on in her thoughts before and after she left. Perhaps she was as surprised as I was by the amount of light and warmth she let in when she opened the door to step into the dark and frosty morning. But of that strange three-day departure, I can say, as Ma did of her book, "She was a real troublin' trip. But she was good."

THE **GO BUS,** A **BOY** AND A **SWASTIKA**

A non-fiction story by Dyanoosh Youssefi,
a Jewish-Iranian student

I was on the Go Bus, on my way home from work. I was
sitting in the back of the bus where two long rows of
seats face each other. Across from me, I saw a boy who
must have been fifteen or sixteen. He was cool, good-
looking. His hair was light brown, almost blond, and it
had a mushroom cut. His light eyes sparkled with vigor
and youth. He was tall, and well-built for his age. (I
imagine that a lot of girls think that he is cute.) He was
listening to his walkman: a teenager, like the rest of us.

Like the rest of us . . . but not quite. There was one
thing that made him different from many of the people I
have known. I could not look away from him or his
knapsack. On his knapsack, he had penned: "Cool rules,"
"Angry as U wanna be," a drawing of what looked like a
little bomb. Having known guys who worshipped Rambo
and Clint Eastwood, I did not think much of these.

Anyhow, it was not these that made me tremble. It was the symbol engraved on the pocket of his knapsack with a bloody red pen. I could not take my eyes off of it. It was a swastika.

At that moment, I felt more intensely than I had felt on many points during our trip. My heart was beating faster than usual and my hands were shaking in shock, anger, and fright.

Of course I had seen swastikas before. One was even spray-painted on the wall of the synagogue right outside my school, not to mention all the movies and the documentaries, the neo-Nazis, skinheads, satan worshippers and the KKK. But there was a young boy who could have been my friend. He looked so innocent. I knew he was. Didn't he know what the symbol meant? Didn't he know how many people died because of it? Didn't he know of the inhumanity and absolute . . . horror and evil that the symbol represented?

I wanted to talk to him. I wanted to ask him if he knew what the swastika, the insignia of Nazi Germany symbolized: an ideology that killed millions of people. In my head, I had a little conversation with him:

"Do you know what that sign symbolizes?" I would hear an answer from him, probably a short one. But I would continue.

"It is the symbol of the Nazis. The people who killed thousands in the war. They put them in ovens. They burned them to death. They gassed them. They made them dig their own graves and then shot them. They shaved people's hair and used it to make clothing. Damn it, how can a guy like you decorate his bag with a swastika? Don't you know what it means?"

I had this "conversation" in my head, though. I am

always hesitant to talk to people for the first time, especially if I am the one starting the conversation.

"But you've got to confront him," I told myself. "You must. Be brave. . . ."

There were only three stops left to my destination. "Do it now or do it never," I threatened myself. Finally, with my heart beating furiously, I looked him in the eye and waved my hand to get his attention.

He looked at me and he smiled. It was a sweet smile.

I thought to myself that he probably knows a bit about the symbol. But he thinks it is cool, like the peace symbol. Hey, if the sign was not representative of so much . . . I would think that it is a neat little sign too. But he just thinks the sign is cool and does not really know. He thinks the sign is cool, and doodles it all over his notes without really knowing the meaning behind it. He does this the way we all do so many things without stopping to look at the meaning behind our actions.

"Can I ask you something?" I said.

Still smiling, he held up his finger, asking me to wait while he turned off his walkman. Then he took the plugs out of his ears. He was polite.

"Why do you have the swastika on your bag?"

He shrugged his shoulders, still smiling.

"Do you know what it symbolizes?"

"Yeah. Nazi Germany." He was still smiling, his eyes sparkling. Did he think that he had impressed me with his knowledge?"

"They killed a lot of people."

"Yeah, I know." His smile was a bit awkward now.

No, what I said did not sound at all the way that I wanted it to.

"They gassed people and burned them in ovens." I

was talking too fast, I think. I continued, however. "I was just there, in the concentration camps, and just seeing that sign now makes me shiver."

He was not smiling anymore, but he did not look penitent either. He just nodded his head a few times and said "O.K." I knew that he must have felt uncomfortable. He said, "O.K.," and leaned back in his seat and put his earplugs back in. I was ready to get up and get off the bus. I wanted to tell him, "Hey, I just wanted you to know. . . . That sign, it isn't anything to be shown off."

But as I got up to leave and stood above the steps, he did not look at me. He looked straight ahead stiffly. As the bus came to a stop, I patted him lightly on the shoulder, and he turned. We smiled at each other, and I got off.

I was upset that I had not really made him understand why it was wrong to put that symbol on a bag. But I did not regret, in fact I felt glad that I spoke to him.

I knew, though, that my "speech" was not enough. He had that sign on his bag because of ignorance: an ignorance that was a result of faulty education; ignorance caused by a generally unaware society; ignorance which could give way to the acceptance of the Zundels; ignorance that could result in the repetition of history.

There are thousands of students, like the guy on the bus, who see in the swastika a symbol as innocuous as a maple leaf. And so, for the first time in my life, I deeply felt compelled to do something to keep the memory of the Holocaust alive—not because I felt that it was my responsibility to do so, but because I saw that boy and the symbol on his bag, cool and meaningless to him and the majority of our generation, but significant and full of horror to others.

BORDERS

A short story by Thomas King,
an aboriginal writer

When I was twelve, maybe thirteen, my mother announced that we were going to go to Salt Lake City to visit my sister who had left the reserve, moved across the line, and found a job. Laetitia had not left home with my mother's blessing, but over time my mother had come to be proud of the fact that Laetitia had done all of this on her own.

"She did real good," my mother would say.

Then there were the fine points to Laetitia's going. She had not, as my mother liked to tell Mrs. Manyfingers, gone floating after some man like a balloon on a string. She hadn't snuck out of the house, either, and gone to Vancouver or Edmonton or Toronto to chase rainbows down alleys. And she hadn't been pregnant.

"She did real good."

I was seven or eight when Laetitia left home. She was

seventeen. Our father was from Rocky Boy on the American side.

"Dad's American," Laetitia told my mother, "so I can go and come as I please."

"Send us a postcard."

Laetitia packed her things, and we headed for the border. Just outside of Milk River, Laetitia told us to watch for the water tower.

"Over the next rise. It's the first thing you see."

"We got a water tower on the reserve," my mother said. "There's a big one in Lethbridge, too."

"You'll be able to see the tops of the flagpoles, too. That's where the border is."

When we got to Coutts, my mother stopped at the convenience store and bought her and Laetitia a cup of coffee. I got an Orange Crush.

"This is real lousy coffee."

"You're just angry because I want to see the world."

"It's the water. From here on down, they got lousy water."

"I can catch the bus from Sweetgrass. You don't have to lift a finger."

"You're going to have to buy your water in bottles if you want good coffee."

There was an old wooden building about a block away, with a tall sign in the yard that said "Museum." Most of the roof had been blown away. Mom told me to go and see when the place was open. There were boards over the windows and doors. You could tell that the place was closed, and I told Mom so, but she said to go and check anyway. Mom and Laetitia stayed by the car. Neither one of them moved. I sat down on the steps of the museum and watched them, and I don't know that they ever said anything to each other. Finally, Laetitia got her bag out of the trunk and gave Mom a hug.

I wandered back to the car. The wind had come up, and it blew Laetitia's hair across her face. Mom reached out and pulled the strands out of Laetitia's eyes, and Laetitia let her.

"You can still see the mountain from here," my mother told Laetitia in Blackfoot.

"Lots of mountains in Salt Lake," Laetitia told her in English.

"The place is closed," I said. "Just like I told you."

Laetitia tucked her hair into her jacket and dragged her bag down the road to the brick building with the American flag flapping on a pole. When she got to where the guards were waiting, she turned, put the bag down, and waved to us. We waved back. Then my mother turned the car around, and we came home.

We got postcards from Laetitia regular, and, if she wasn't spreading jelly on the truth, she was happy. She found a good job and rented an apartment with a pool.

"And she can't even swim," my mother told Mrs. Manyfingers.

Most of the postcards said we should come down and see the city, but whenever I mentioned this, my mother would stiffen up.

So I was surprised when she bought two new tires for the car and put on her blue dress with the green and yellow flowers. I had to dress up, too, for my mother did not want us crossing the border looking like Americans. We made sandwiches and put them in a big box with pop and potato chips and some apples and bananas and a big jar of water.

"But we can stop at one of those restaurants, too, right?"

"We maybe should take some blankets in case you get sleepy."

"But we can stop at one of those restaurants, too, right?"

The border was actually two towns, though neither one was big enough to amount to anything. Coutts was on the Canadian side and consisted of the convenience store and gas station, the museum that was closed and boarded up, and a motel. Sweetgrass was on the American side, but all you could see was an overpass that arched across the highway and disappeared into the prairies. Just hearing the names of these towns, you would expect that Sweetgrass, which is a nice name and sounds like it is related to other places such as Medicine Hat and Moose Jaw and Kicking Horse Pass, would be on the Canadian side, and that Coutts, which sounds abrupt and rude, would be on the American side. But this was not the case.

Between the two borders was a duty-free shop where you could buy cigarettes and liquor and flags. Stuff like that.

We left the reserve in the morning and drove until we got to Coutts.

"Last time we stopped here," my mother said, "you had an Orange Crush. You remember that?"

"Sure," I said. "That was when Laetitia took off."

"You want another Orange Crush?"

"That means we're not going to stop at a restaurant, right?"

My mother got a coffee at the convenience store, and we stood around and watched the prairies move in the sunlight. Then we climbed back in the car. My mother straightened the dress across her thighs, leaned against the wheel, and drove all the way to the border in first gear, slowly, as if she were trying to see through a bad storm or riding high on black ice.

The border guard was an old guy. As he walked to the car, he swayed from side to side, his feet set wide apart, the holster on his hip pitching up and down. He leaned into the window, looked into the back seat, and looked at my mother and me.

"Morning, ma'am."

"Good morning."

"Where you heading?"

"Salt Lake City."

"Purpose of your visit?"

"Visit my daughter."

"Citizenship"

"Blackfoot," my mother told him.

"Ma'am?"

"Blackfoot," my mother repeated.

"Canadian?"

"Blackfoot."

It would have been easier if my mother had just said "Canadian" and been done with it, but I could see she wasn't going to do that. The guard wasn't angry or anything. He smiled and looked towards the building. Then he turned back and nodded.

"Morning, ma'am."

"Good morning."

"Any firearms or tobacco?"

"No."

"Citizenship?"

"Blackfoot."

He told us to sit in the car and wait, and we did. In about

five minutes, another guard came out with the first man. They were talking as they came, both men swaying back and forth like two cowboys headed for a bar or a gunfight.

"Morning, ma'am."

"Good morning."

"Cecil tells me you and the boy are Blackfoot."

"That's right."

"Now, I know that we got Blackfeet on the American side and the Canadians got Blackfeet on their side. Just so we can keep our records straight, what side do you come from?"

I knew exactly what my mother was going to say, and I could have told them if they had asked me.

"Canadian side or American side?" asked the guard.

"Blackfoot side," she said.

It didn't take them long to lose their sense of humour, I can tell you that. The one guard stopped smiling altogether and told us to park our car at the side of the building and come in.

We sat on a wood bench for about an hour before anyone came over to talk to us. This time it was a woman. She had a gun, too.

"Hi," she said. "I'm Inspector Pratt. I understand there is a little misunderstanding."

"I'm going to visit my daughter in Salt Lake City," my mother told her, "We don't have any guns or beer."

"It's a legal technicality, that's all."

"My daughter's Blackfoot, too."

The woman opened a briefcase and took out a couple of forms and began to write on one of them. "Everyone who crosses our border has to declare their citizenship. Even Americans. It helps us keep track of the visitors we get from the various countries."

She went on like that for maybe fifteen minutes, and a

lot of the stuff she told us was interesting.

"I can understand how you feel about having to tell us your citizenship, and here's what I'll do. You tell me, and I won't put it down on the form. No-one will know but you and me."

Her gun was silver. There were several chips in the wood handle and the name "Stella" was scratched into the metal butt.

We were in the border office for about four hours, and we talked to almost everyone there. One of the men bought me a Coke. My mother brought a couple of sandwiches in from the car. I offered a part of mine to Stella, but she said she wasn't hungry.

I told Stella that we were Blackfoot and Canadian, but she said that that didn't count because I was a minor. In the end, she told us that if my mother didn't declare her citizenship, we would have to go back where we came from. My mother stood up and thanked Stella for her time. Then we got back in the car and drove to the Canadian border, which was only about a hundred yards away.

I was disappointed. I hadn't seen Laetitia for a long time, and I had never been to Salt Lake City. When she was still at home, Laetitia would go on and on about Salt Lake City. She had never been there, but her boyfriend Lester Tallbull had spent a year in Salt Lake at a technical school.

"It's a great place," Lester would say. "Nothing but blondes in the whole state."

Whenever he said that, Laetitia would slug him on his shoulder hard enough to make him flinch. He had some brochures on Salt Lake and some maps, and every so often the two of them would spread them out on the table.

"That's the temple. It's right downtown. You got to have a pass to get in."

"Charlotte says anyone can go in and look around."

"When was Charlotte in Salt Lake? Just when the hell was Charlotte in Salt Lake?"

"Last year."

"This is Liberty Park. It's got a zoo. There's good skiing in the mountains."

"Got all the skiing we can use," my mother would say. "People come from all over the world to ski at Banff. Cardston's got a temple, if you like those kinds of things."

"Oh, this one is real big," Lester would say. "They got armed guards and everything."

"Not what Charlotte says."

"What does she know?"

Lester and Laetitia broke up, but I guess the idea of Salt Lake stuck in her mind.

The Canadian border guard was a young woman, and she seemed happy to see us.

"Hi," she said. "You folks sure have a great day for a trip. Where are you coming from?"

"Standoff."

"Is that in Montana?"

"No."

"Where are you going?"

"Standoff."

The woman's name was Carol and I don't guess she was any older than Laetitia. "Wow, you both Canadians?"

"Blackfoot."

"Really? I have a friend I went to school with who is Blackfoot. Do you know Mike Harley?"

"No."

"He went to school in Lethbridge, but he's really from Browning."

It was a nice conversation and there were no cars behind us, so there was no rush.

"You're not bringing any liquor back, are you?"

"No."

"Any cigarettes or plants or stuff like that?"

"No."

"Citizenship?"

"Blackfoot."

"I know," said the woman, "and I'd be proud of being Blackfoot if I were Blackfoot. But you have to be American or Canadian."

When Laetitia and Lester broke up, Lester took his brochures and maps with him, so Laetitia wrote to someone in Salt Lake City, and, about a month later, she got a big envelope of stuff. We sat at the table and opened up all the brochures, and Laetitia read each one out loud.

"Salt Lake City is the gateway to some of the world's most magnificent skiing.

"Salt Lake City is the home of one of the newest professional basketball franchises, the Utah Jazz.

"The Great Salt Lake is one of the natural wonders of the world."

It was kind of exciting seeing all those colour brochures on the table and listening to Laetitia read all about how Salt Lake City was one of the best places in the entire world.

"That Salt Lake City place sounds too good to be true," my mother told her.

"It has everything."

"We got everything right here."

"It's boring here."

"People in Salt Lake City are probably sending away

for brochures of Calgary and Lethbridge and Pincher Creek right now."

In the end, my mother would say that maybe Laetitia should go to Salt Lake City, and Laetitia would say that maybe she would.

We parked the car to the side of the building and Carol led us into a small room on the second floor. I found a comfortable spot on the couch and flipped through some back issues of *Saturday Night* and *Alberta Report*.

When I woke up, my mother was just coming out of another office. She didn't say a word to me. I followed her down the stairs and out to the car. I thought we were going home, but she turned the car around and drove back towards the American border, which made me think we were going to visit Laetitia in Salt Lake City after all. Instead she pulled into the parking lot of the duty-free store and stopped.

"We going to see Laetitia?"

"No."

"We going home?"

Pride is a good thing to have, you know. Laetitia had a lot of pride, and so did my mother. I figured that some-day, I'd have it, too.

"So where are we going?"

Most of that day, we wandered around the duty-free store, which wasn't very large. The manager had a name tag with a tiny American flag on one side and tiny Canadian flag on the other. His name was Mel. Towards evening, he began suggesting that we should be on our way. I told him we had nowhere to go, that neither the Americans nor the Canadians would let us in. He laughed at that and told us that we should buy something or leave.

The car was not very comfortable, but we did have all that food and it was April, so even if it did snow as it sometimes does on the prairies, we wouldn't freeze. The next morning my mother drove to the American border.

It was a different guard this time, but the questions were the same. We didn't spend as much time in the office as we had the day before. By noon, we were back at the Canadian border. By two we were back in the duty-free shop parking lot.

The second night in the car was not as much fun as the first, but my mother seemed in good spirits, and, all in all, it was as much an adventure as an inconvenience. There wasn't much food left and that was a problem, but we had lots of water as there was a faucet at the side of the duty-free shop.

One Sunday, Laetitia and I were watching television. Mom was over at Mrs. Manyfingers's. Right in the middle of the programme, Laetitia turned off the set and said she was going to Salt Lake City, that life around here was too boring. I had wanted to see the rest of the programme and really didn't care if Laetitia went to Salt Lake City or not. When Mom got home, I told her what Laetitia had said.

What surprised me was how angry Laetitia got when she found out that I had told Mom.

"You got a big mouth."

"That's what you said."

"What I said is none of your business."

"I didn't say anything."

"Well, I'm going for sure, now."

That weekend, Laetitia packed her bags, and we drove her to the border.

Mel turned out to be friendly. When he closed up for the night and found us still parked in the lot, he came over and asked us if our car was broken down or something. My mother thanked him for his concern and told him that we were fine, that things would get straightened out in the morning.

"You're kidding," said Mel. "You'd think they could handle the simple things."

"We got some apples and a banana," I said, "but we're all out of ham sandwiches."

"You know, you read about these things, but you just don't believe it. You just don't believe it."

"Hamburgers would be even better because they got more stuff for energy."

My mother slept in the back seat. I slept in the front because I was smaller and could lie under the steering wheel. Late that night, I heard my mother open the car door. I found her sitting on her blanket leaning against the bumper of the car.

"You see all those stars," she said. "When I was a little girl, my grandmother used to take me and my sisters out on the prairies and tell us stories about all the stars."

"Do you think Mel is going to bring us any hamburgers?"

"Every one of those stars has a story. You see that bunch of stars over there that look like a fish?"

"He didn't say no."

"Coyote went fishing, one day. That's how it all started." We sat out under the stars that night, and my mother told me all sorts of stories. She was serious about it, too. She'd tell them slow, repeating parts as she went, as if she expected me to remember each one.

Early the next morning, the television vans began to

arrive, and guys in suits and women in dresses came trot-
ting over to us, dragging microphones and cameras and
lights behind them. One of the vans had a table set up with
orange juice and sandwiches and fruit. It was for the crew,
but when I told them we hadn't eaten for a while, a really
skinny blonde woman told us we could eat as much as we
wanted.

They mostly talked to my mother. Every so often one
of the reporters would come over and ask me questions
about how it felt to be an Indian without a country. I told
them we had a nice house on the reserve and that my
cousins had a couple of horses we rode when we went fishing. Some of the television people went over to the American border, and then they went to the Canadian border.

Around noon, a good-looking guy in a dark blue suit
and an orange tie with little ducks on it drove up in a fancy
car. He talked to my mother for a while, and, after they
were done talking, my mother called me over, and we got
into our car. Just as my mother started the engine, Mel
came over and gave us a bag of peanut brittle and told us
that justice was a damn hard thing to get, but that we
shouldn't give up.

I would have preferred lemon drops, but it was nice of
Mel anyway.

"Where are we going now?"

"Going to visit Laetitia."

The guard who came out to our car was all smiles. The
television lights were so bright they hurt my eyes, and, if
you tried to look through the windshield in certain direc-
tions, you couldn't see a thing.

"Morning, ma'am."

"Good morning."

"Where you heading?"

"Salt Lake City."

"Purpose of your visit?"

"Visit my daughter."

"Any tobacco, liquor, or firearms?"

"Don't smoke."

"Any plants or fruit?"

"Not any more."

"Citizenship?"

"Blackfoot."

The guard rocked back on his heels and jammed his thumbs into his gun belt. "Thank you," he said, his fingers patting the butt of the revolver. "Have a pleasant trip."

My mother rolled the car forward, and the television people had to scramble out of the way. They ran alongside the car as we pulled away from the border, and, when they couldn't run any farther, they stood in the middle of the highway and waved and waved and waved.

We got to Salt Lake City the next day. Laetitia was happy to see us, and, that first night, she took us out to a restaurant that made really good soups. The list of pies took up a whole page. I had cherry. Mom had chocolate. Laetitia said that she saw us on television the night before and, during the meal, she had us tell her the story over and over again.

Laetitia took us everywhere. We went to a fancy ski resort. We went to the temple. We got to go shopping in a couple of large malls, but they weren't as large as the one in Edmonton, and Mom said so.

After a week or so, I got bored and wasn't at all sad when my mother said we should be heading back home. Laetitia wanted us to stay longer, but Mom said no, that she had things to do back home and that, next time, Laetitia should come up and visit. Laetitia said she was thinking about moving back, and Mom told her to do as she pleased, and Laetitia said that she would.

On the way home, we stopped at the duty-free shop, and my mother gave Mel a green hat that said "Salt Lake" across the front. Mel was a funny guy. He took the hat and blew his nose and told my mother that she was an inspiration to us all. He gave us some more peanut brittle and came out into the parking lot and waved at us all the way to the Canadian border.

It was almost evening when we left Coutts. I watched the border through the rear window until all you could see were the tops of the flagpoles and the blue water tower, and then they rolled over a hill and disappeared.

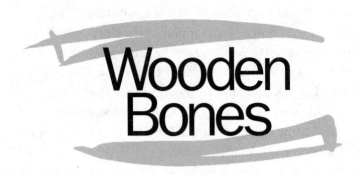

Wooden Bones

A short story
by Charles de Lint

"I really don't need this," Liz said.

She was standing in front of her uncle's house, look-ing around at the clutter that filled the front yard. What a mess. There was an old car with one door sagging open, stacks of pink insulation, tools and scrap wood, a bat-tered RV, sheets of Styrofoam and Black Joe, a discarded sink—all the debris of a handyman's livelihood and then some, left out to the weather.

Tom Bohay, her uncle, had a renovation business that he ran from the family farm—a hundred acres set right on the Big Rideau Lake. The lake was a hundred yards from the back of the house, which was in the middle of being renovated itself; had been for the past two years, ever since the farmhouse up on the hill burned down and, rather than rebuild, her uncle decided to fix up what had been an oversized cottage. According to Liz's mom, Tom was real good at working on other people's places, but not so hot when it came to the home front.

Staying here was going to be like living in a junkyard. Liz felt as though she were on the set of *Sanford and Son,* except it was worse, because there wasn't any urban sprawl beyond the property. No downtown or malls or anyplace interesting at all. Instead it was out in the middle of nowhere. Pasture and bush and rocky hillsides. A neighbor kept cows on the hilly pasture between the road leading into the farm and the house. If you went for a walk anywhere past the yard itself, you had to watch that you didn't step in a cow pie.

Wonderful stuff.

"I *really* don't need this," she repeated.

"Need what?" her cousin asked, coming up behind her.

Standing together, the two girls presented a picture of opposites. Annie Bohay wore her long dark hair pulled back in a ponytail. She had a roundish face, with large brown eyes that gave her the look of an owl. Her taste in clothing leaned toward baggy jeans, running shoes, and T-shirts, none of which did much for her plump figure. In contrast, Liz was bony and thin, her own jeans tight, her black leather boots narrow-toed and scuffed, her T-shirt cut off at the shoulders and emblazoned with a screaming skull's head and the words Mötley Crüe, her blond hair short and spiky.

"Any of this," she said, waving an arm that took in the whole of the farm.

"Aw, c'mon," Annie said. "It's not so bad."

Maybe not if you don't know any better, Liz thought, but she tactfully kept that to herself. After all, she was stuck here for the summer. No point in alienating her cousin, who was probably going to be her only contact with anyone even remotely her age for the next three months.

Yesterday Annie had taken her on a tour of the property. They'd gone around a wooded point that jutted out into the lake until they came to a sandy beach—the swimming was good off the dock near the house, but the shore was all rocky—and then up to a plateau that Annie called "the Moon." The name made sense, Liz thought when they got there. The broad hilltop was a wide, flat expanse of white marble limestone, spring-fed pools, and junipers, enclosed by stands of apple trees, that had a real otherworldly feel to it.

From the Moon they went down another steep slope to a cow path leading back to the house. Instead of going back home when the path joined the lane, however, Annie took Liz the other way, up the lane with the cow pastures on either side, back to the road leading into the farm. Here there were the rusted hulks of abandoned farm machinery and the remains of outbuildings and barns that looked, to Liz's city eyes, like the skeletons of ancient behemoths, vast wooden rib cages lifting from the fields to towering heights.

The grass on either side of the lane was cropped short, and dotted with cow pies and thistles standing upright like steadfast little soldiers. At the very top of the hill where the lane met the road under a canopy of enormous trees was an old barn that had survived the years still mostly in one piece. It had a fieldstone foundation and gray weathered wood for its timbers and planking.

Inside it was mysteriously shadowed, with a thick flooring of old hay bales at one end, wooden boards at the other. What light entered came through places where side boards were missing—sudden shafts of sunlight that made the shadows even darker. Liz found the place fascinating and creepy, all at the same time.

From there they headed straight down to the lake and followed the shore back home, and that was it. The end of the tour.

Surprisingly, Liz had enjoyed herself, exploring and wandering about; but that first evening after supper, she looked out the window at the dark fields—it was so dark in the country—and realized that this was it. In one afternoon she'd done everything there was to do. So what was she going to do for the rest of the summer?

Because she was stuck here. Abandoned just like the rusted machinery and outbuildings up on the hill.

Things had been going from bad to worse for Liz over the past couple of years. On Christmas Eve, when she was twelve, her father had walked out on her and her mother, and they hadn't heard a word from him in the two years since. At first his departure had been a relief from all the shouting and fighting that had gone on. But then her mother started drinking, bringing boyfriends home—a different one every weekend—and Liz had ended up spending more time crashing with friends or just wandering the streets than at home.

Then her mother got a job in a hotel out in Banff.

"It's just for the summer," she'd explained to Liz. "I know it doesn't seem fair, but if you come with me, we'll end up spending all the extra money that I was hoping to save for us for this winter. You don't mind staying with Aunt Emma, do you?"

At fourteen, Liz had long since realized, you don't have any rights. And there were times you just didn't argue. Especially not after what she'd overheard her mother telling her latest boyfriend just the night before.

"What do you do with a kid like her? She's out of control, and I don't know what to do with her anymore. I've got to have some life of my own. Is that so very wrong?"

Naturally, the boyfriend told her she was doing the right thing and, "C'mon, baby. Let's party now."

Right.

It hurt. She wasn't going to pretend it didn't. But at least she hadn't cried.

I sure hope life gets better, Liz thought, standing with her cousin now in the front yard. Because if it doesn't, then I'm out of here. I can't take any more.

She could feel a burning behind her eyes, but she blinked fiercely until it went away. You've just got to tough it out, she told herself as she turned to look at Annie.

"So what do you want to do?" she asked her cousin.

Annie pointed to a heap of recently split firewood. "Well, Dad asked me to get that stacked today. Do you want to help?"

Liz's heart sank, but she kept a smile on her lips. Of course. They cooked on a wood stove, heated the place with it in the winter. Only why would anybody *choose* to live like this?

"Sure," she said. "Sounds like fun." She spoke the words cheerfully enough, but the look on her face added: About as much fun as banging my head against a wall.

There was really *nothing* to do in the evenings. The TV was a twelve-inch black-and-white that was kept in her aunt and uncle's bedroom. To watch it, you had to sit on the bed with them—not exactly Liz's scene, though Annie didn't seem to mind. Of course, they were her parents. Liz had brought some cassettes with her, but her boom box was broken and the amp here only worked on one channel. Besides, nobody cared much for Bon Jovi or Van Halen, much less the Cult or some hard-core heavy metal.

Definitely a musical wasteland.

That night, after staring at the walls for about as long as she could take, she announced that she was going out for a walk.

"I don't think that's such a good idea," her aunt began.

"Give the girl some slack," her uncle broke in. "How's she going to get into trouble out here? You just keep to the lane," he added to Liz. "It gets darker in the country than you'll be used to, and it's easy to get lost."

"I'll be careful," Liz said, willing to promise anything just to get out of there for a few moments.

Get lost, she thought when she was standing outside. Sure. As if there weren't a million side roads whichever way you turned. But it was dark. As soon as she left the yard and its spotlights, the night closed in on either side of her. Moonless, with clouds shrouding the stars, there wasn't much to see at all. A pinprick of uneasiness stole up her spine.

She looked back at the well-lit yard; it didn't seem nearly so bad now. Kind of comforting, really. She was of half a mind to just plunk herself down in the front seat of the old car with its door hanging ajar, when she cocked her head. What was that sound?

She turned slowly, and a glimmer of light on top of the hill near the road caught her eye. It came from the barn, a dim yellow glow against the darkness. And the sound was coming from there as well. A fiddle playing something that sounded a little like country music, only it wasn't quite the same. There was no way a bunch of hokey guys in rhinestone outfits were playing this stuff.

Curious, her fear forgotten, Liz started up the lane, crossing over the field when she was opposite the barn. She walked carefully, eyes on the ground as she tried to spot the cow pies. The fiddling was louder now, an infectious sound.

When she reached the outer wall of the barn, her nervousness returned. Who was out here, playing music in an old barn in the middle of the night? It was a little too weird. But having come this far . . .

She stood on her tiptoes to peer through a broken slat and blinked with surprise. Everything was different inside. An oil lamp lit row upon row of wooden carnival horses, all leaning against each other along one side of the barn. Their polished finish gleamed in the lamplight, heads cocked as though they were listening to the music. Their painted eyes seemed to turn in her direction. Sitting facing them, with his back to her, was the man playing the fiddle. He had a floppy wide-brimmed black hat from which two chestnut-and-pink ribbons dangled. His clothes were so patched that it was hard to tell what their original color had been.

Close as she was, with the barn magnifying and echoing the music, it sounded to Liz as though there were more than one fiddler playing. She could also hear a tap-tapping sound which, she realized as she looked more closely, came from the man's bootheels where they kept the tune's rhythm on the old barn's wooden floor.

When the tune ended, Liz wondered if she should say hello or just hang out here, listening. It was kind of neat, this—

The man turned just then and all rational thought fled. Those weren't ribbons hanging down from under his hat. They were ears. Because his face was a rabbit's: big brown eyes, twitching nose, protruding jaw. The bizarreness of what she was seeing made her head spin.

She scrambled back, a scream building up in her throat. Turning, she fled, stumbled, fell. As she tried to scrabble to her feet, a big black wave came washing over her and the world just went away as though someone had thrown its switch from on to off.

When she finally blinked her eyes open, she found herself lying on the grass in front of her uncle's house, screaming. The front door burst open and her uncle and aunt were there.

"There was . . . there was . . ." Liz tried to explain, pointing back toward the hilltop barn, but there were no lights up there now. No music drifting down the hill. And how had she gotten all the way down here anyway? The last thing she remembered was turning away from the grotesque face. . . .

She let her uncle help her into the house. Annie and her aunt put her to bed. Lying in the upstairs loft that she was sharing with Annie, she could hear her aunt and uncle arguing down below.

"I tell you she's on drugs, and I won't have it," her aunt was saying. "Not in this house. I know she's your sister's daughter, Tom, but—"

"She just got scared," her uncle said. "That's all. City kid. Probably heard a coon rustling around in the brush and thought it was a bear."

"She's trouble. I don't see why we have to look at that sullen face all summer long."

"Because she's family," her uncle said, his voice angry. "That's why. We don't turn away family."

Liz pushed her hands against her ears, shutting out the voices. The features of that rabbit-faced fiddler rose up to haunt her as soon as she closed her eyes. I don't do drugs, she thought. So I've got to be going crazy.

Liz was very subdued in the following days. She tried to stay on her best behavior—smiling, helping out where she could. She was scared about a lot of things. If her aunt and uncle kicked her out, they sure weren't going to put her on the bus back to Toronto and let her go her own merry way. They'd call her mother, and her mother was going to be really mad. She'd threatened often enough to turn Liz over to Children's Aid because she just couldn't handle her. Who knew where she'd end up if that happened?

And then there was the fiddler.

He haunted her. At first, thinking back, she decided that she'd just seen some flaky tramp wearing a Halloween mask. Only the features had seemed too real—she had an inexplicable certainty that they were real—and there'd been something too weird about the whole situation for her to believe that she'd just made it up. She kept hearing his music, seeing his face.

Up on the Moon with Annie one day, she thought she heard the strains of his fiddle again, but when she asked Annie *she'd* heard anything, her cousin just gave her a strange look.

"Like what?"

"Some kind of music—fiddle music."

Annie grinned and leaned conspiratorially closer. "He hides in the trees, a big old bear of a man, smelling like a swamp and playing his fiddle, trying to lure unwary travelers close so that he can chew on their bones."

Liz shivered. "Really?"

"Of course not!" Annie said, shaking her head. "That's just a story the old-timers spread around. People sometimes hear music out in the woods around here—or at least they think they do. It's been going on for years, but it's just the wind in the trees or blowing through a hole in a fence or a barn."

"These old-timers . . . do they ever tell stories about an old tramp with the head of a rabbit playing that fiddle?"

"Get serious."

But Liz kept hearing the music. Or they'd be down by the lake and she would spot a rabbit looking out at them from a cedar stand—a big rabbit, its fur the same odd chestnut color of the fiddler's ears. Its eyes too human for comfort. Watching her. Considering.

She *had* to be going crazy.

Finally, she just couldn't take it anymore. A week after the night she'd first seen him, she waited until everybody else had turned in, then got dressed and crept out of the house. Looking up the hill to the barn, she could see the dull glow of lantern light coming from between its broken side boards, but there was no music. Chewing her lip, she started up the hill.

When she reached the barn, she had to stand for a long moment, trying to calm the rapid drum of her heartbeat. This is nuts, the sensible part of her said. Yeah, she thought. I know. But I've got to see it through. Taking a deep breath, she walked around to the side of the barn that faced the road and stepped in through the doorway.

Except for the lack of music, it was all the same as it had been the other night. The oil lamp hanging from the crossbeam, throwing off its yellow light. The rows of wooden carnival horses. The fiddler, his instrument set down on a bale of hay beside him, was still dressed in his raggedy patched clothes. His floppy hat was lying beside his fiddle. He was carving a piece of wood with a long, sharp knife and looked up to where she stood, not saying a word.

Trying not to look at the knife, Liz swallowed dryly. Now that she was here, she didn't know why she'd come. That wasn't a mask he was wearing. It was real. The twitch of the nose. The sly look in those eyes.

"Wh-what do you . . . want from me?" she managed finally.

The fiddler stopped carving. "What makes you think I want something?"

"I . . . you . . . You're haunting me. Everywhere I turn, I see your face. Hear your music."

The fiddler shrugged. "That's not so strange. I live around here. Why shouldn't we meet in passing?"

"Nobody else sees you."

"Maybe they're not looking properly. You new people are like that a lot."

"New people?"

The rabbit-man grinned. "That's what we call you." The grin faded. "We're the ones who were here first. Everything changed when you came."

"What's your name?"

"Is a name so important?"

"Sure. Or how does anybody know who you are?"

"I know who I am, and that's enough."

Oddly enough, the more they talked, the more at ease Liz began to feel. It was like being in a dream where, because of its context, you didn't question anything. The weirdest things made sense. She sat down on a broad wooden beam across from the fiddler, her feet dangling, heels tapping against the wood.

"But what do other people call you?" she asked.

"Your people or my people?"

"Whichever."

For a long moment the fiddler said nothing. He took out a tobacco pouch and rolled a cigarette, lit it. Gray-blue smoke wreathed around his head when he exhaled.

"Let me tell you a story," he said. "There was once a girl who lived with her parents in a house in the city. One day her father went away and never came back, and she thought it was because of her. Her mother had a picture in her head as to what the girl should be, and she never let up trying to fit the girl's odd angles into the perfect mold she had sitting there in her head, and the girl thought because she didn't fit, that was her fault, too.

"But she had a will of her own, and maybe she didn't know exactly what she wanted to be, but she wanted to be able to find out on her own what it was, not have everyone else tell her what it should be. So when someone said one thing, she did another. She wore a frown so much that she forgot how to smile. And all the time she was carrying around this baggage in her head. Useless stuff.

"The baggage was like the rot that gets into an old tree sometimes. Eventually, it just ate her away, and there was nothing left of her that she could call her own. On that day, the people around her put her in a box and stuck her in the ground, and that's where she is to this day."

Liz stared at him. A coldness sat in her chest, making it hard to breathe.

"You . . . you're talking about me," she said. "About what I've been . . . what's going to happen to me."

The fiddler shrugged. "It's just a story."

"But I can't help it. Nobody ever gives me a chance."

"The old people—my people—we make our own chances."

"Easy for you to say. You're not fourteen with

everybody running your life. I don't have any rights."

"Everybody's got rights. Take responsibility for what's yours, and let the rest slide. It's not always easy, but it's not that hard once you learn the trick of it."

"But it hurts."

The fiddler nodded. "I know."

Liz stared down at her boots, trying to understand what was going on. The fiddler carefully butted out his cigarette and put the dead butt in his pocket. Picking up his instrument, he began to play.

Liz heard things in that music. Her father's voice, her mother's voice. Her aunt, her teachers. The policeman who'd caught her shoplifting. Everybody saying she was no good until she began to believe it herself, until she wore the part and made it true.

But when she closed her eyes and really listened to the music, images flooded her mind. She saw her uncle's farm as a place where two worlds met. Once world was that of the new people, her people; the other was that of those who'd been here first. The old people, the first people.

Lost things from her world found a home in the world of the old people, the music told her. And in this part of that old world their keeper was a man with the face of a rabbit who didn't have a name. He looked after lost things. Like the carousel horses; sleeping at night, prancing through the fields by day. Liz knew she couldn't see them in the barn when she was in her own world, but they were here all the same. The old people made the lost welcome—for some the old world became their home; for others it was a resting place until they could go on again.

Lost things. Lost people. Like her.

It was kind of magic—maybe real, maybe not, but that didn't matter. They were what they were, just like she had to be what she was. The best that she could be—not the image that others had of her. Not weighted down with a baggage of anger and guilt.

She blinked when the music stopped. Looking up, she saw that the fiddler had laid aside his instrument once more. He had his knife out again and had gone back to carving the piece of wood he'd been working on when she first arrived.

"What kind of music is that?" she asked.

"I heard it from the first new people who came here—got my fiddle from one of them."

It had a sound like nothing Liz had ever heard before. A depth. Where heavy metal just walled away her feelings behind its head-banging thunder, this music seemed to draw those feelings out so that she could deal with them instead.

"It sounds really . . . special," she said.

The fiddler nodded. "Needs something more, though." He held up the carving and studied it in the lamplight. "Looks about right." Taking a twin to it from his pocket, he held the two curved pieces of wood between his fingers and moved his arm in a shaking motion. The pieces of wood rattled rhythmically against each other, sending up a clickety-clack that echoed comfortably in the old barn.

"Here," he said, handing them over to her and showing her how to hold them. "You give it a try."

"What are they?"

"Bones. Wooden bones. They're usually made from ribs of animals, but I like the sound of the wood, so I make them from the ribs of the old barns instead."

When Liz tried to copy his movement, one of the bones fell from her hand. She gave an embarrassed shrug.

Picking up the fallen one, she started to hand them back to the fiddler, but he shook his head.

"I can't make them work," she said.

"That's because you've hardly given them a try. Take them with you. Practice. It's like everything else—takes a little work to make it go right."

Like life, Liz thought. She closed her fingers around the bones.

"All right," she said. "I will."

The fiddler smiled. "That's right. Build on the hurt. Let it temper who you become instead of wearing you down. It's not always easy, but it's—"

"Not that hard once you learn the trick of it?"

"Exactly. Time you were going."

"But—" Liz began.

Before she could finish, she felt a sense of vertigo. She shut her eyes. When she opened them again, she was standing in front of her uncle's house, blinking in the spotlights that lit up the yard, a pair of wooden bones clutched in her hand. She looked up to the old barn, dark and quiet on the top of the hill.

A dream? she asked herself. Had it all been just a dream? But she still had these. She lifted her hand, looking at the gleam of the wooden bones she was still holding.

"Will I ever see you again?" she asked.

"Look for me, and I'll be there," a voice said softly in her ear. "Listen, and you'll hear me."

She started and turned sharply, but there was no one there. Placing the bones between her fingers the way he'd shown her, she gave an experimental shake of her hands. Still nothing. But she wasn't going to give up. Not with these. Not with anything.

THE
Blanket

A short story
by Floyd Dell

Petey hadn't really believed that Dad would be doing
it—sending Granddad away. "Away" was what they were
all calling it. Not until now could he believe it of Dad.

But here was the blanket that Dad had that day
bought for him, and in the morning he'd be going away.
And this was the last evening they'd be having together.
Dad was off seeing that girl he was to marry. He'd not be
back till late, and they could sit up and talk.

It was a fine September night, with a thin white
moon riding high over the gully. When they'd washed up
the supper dishes they went out on the shanty porch, the
old man and the bit of a boy, taking their chairs. "I'll get
me fiddle," said the old man, "and play ye some of the
old tunes." But instead of the fiddle he brought out the
blanket. It was a big double blanket, red, with black
cross stripes.

"Now, isn't that a fine blanket!" said the old man, smoothing it over his knees. "And isn't your father a kind man to be giving the old fellow a blanket like that to go away with? It cost something, it did—look at the wool of it! And warm it will be these cold winter nights to come. There'll be few blankets there the equal of this one!"

It was like Granddad to be saying that. He was trying to make it easier. He'd pretended all along it was he that was wanting to go away to the great brick building—the government place, where he'd be with so many other old fellows having the best of everything. . . . But Petey hadn't believed Dad would really do it, until this night when he brought home the blanket.

"Oh, yes, it's a fine blanket," said Petey, and got up and went into the shanty. He wasn't the kind to cry, and, besides, he was too old for that, being eleven. He'd just come in to fetch Granddad's fiddle.

The blanket slid to the floor as the old man took the fiddle and stood up. It was the last night they'd be having together. There wasn't any need to say, "Play all the old tunes." Granddad tuned up for a minute, and then said, "This is one you'll like to remember."

The thin moon was high overhead, and there was a gentle breeze playing down the gully. He'd never be hearing Granddad play like this again. It was as well Dad was moving into that new house, away from here. He'd not want, Petey wouldn't, to sit here on the old porch of fine evenings, with Granddad gone.

The tune changed. "Here's something gayer." Petey sat and stared out over the gully. Dad would marry that girl. Yes, that girl who'd kissed him and slobbered over him, saying she'd try to be a good mother to him, and all. . . . His chair creaked as he involuntarily gave his body a painful twist.

The tune stopped suddenly, and Granddad said: "It's a poor tune, except to be dancing to." And then: "It's a fine girl your father's going to marry. He'll be feeling young again, with a pretty wife like that. And what would an old fellow like me be doing around their house, getting in the way, an old nuisance, what with my talk of aches and pains! And then there'll be babies coming, and I'd not want to be there to hear them crying at all hours. It's best that I take myself off, like I'm doing. One more tune or two, and then we'll be going to bed to get some sleep against the morning, when I'll pack up my fine blanket and take my leave. Listen to this, will you? It's a bit sad, but a fine tune for a night like this."

They didn't hear the two people coming down the gully path, Dad and the pretty girl with the hard, bright face like a china doll's. But they heard her laugh, right by the porch, and the tune stopped on a wrong, high, startled note. Dad didn't say anything, but the girl came forward and spoke to Granddad prettily: "I'll not be seeing you leave in the morning, so I came over to say good-by."

"It's kind of you," said Granddad, with his eyes cast down; and then, seeing the blanket at his feet, he stopped to pick it up. "And will you look at this," said in embarrassment, "the fine blanket my son has given me to go away with!"

"Yes," she said, "it's a fine blanket." She felt of the wool, and repeated in surprise, "A fine blanket—I'll say it is!" She turned to Dad, and said to him coldly, "It cost something, that."

He cleared his throat, and said defensively. "I wanted him to have the best. . . ."

The girl stood there, still intent on the blanket. "It's

double, too," she said reproachfully to Dad.

"Yes," said Granddad, "it's double—a fine blanket for an old fellow to be going away with."

The boy went abruptly into the shanty. He was looking for something. He could hear that girl reproaching Dad, and Dad becoming angry in his slow way. And now she was suddenly going away in a huff. . . . As Petey came out, she turned and called back, "All the same, he doesn't need a double blanket!" And she ran up the gully path.

Dad was looking after her uncertainly.

"Oh, she's right," said the boy coldly. "Here, Dad"— and he held out a pair of scissors. "Cut the blanket in two."

Both of them stared at the boy, startled. "Cut it in two, I tell you, Dad!" he cried out. "And keep the other half!"

"That's not a bad idea," said Granddad gently. "I don't need so much of a blanket."

"Yes," said the boy harshly, "a single blanket's enough for an old man when he's sent away. We'll save the other half, Dad; it will come in handy later."

"Now what do you mean by that?" asked Dad.

"I mean," said the boy slowly, "that I'll give it to you, Dad—when you're old and I'm sending you—away."

There was a silence, and then Dad went over to Granddad and stood before him, not speaking. But Granddad understood, for he put out a hand and laid it on Dad's shoulder. Petey was watching them. And he heard Granddad whisper, "It's all right, son—I knew you didn't mean it. . . ." And then Petey cried.

But it didn't matter—because they were all three crying together.

With a Little Gold Pencil

A short story
by Barbara Girion

I had been a reporter for Union High's paper since my freshman year. Now, as a junior, I was features editor and doing everything possible to make sure I was appointed editor-in-chief for my senior year.

I knew that the way to keep ahead of the competition was to come up with super ideas, and this year I'd hit on a winner. I had started a personality news column called "Shelby Sez," with my picture at the top. That's me, Shelby Dreighton, age seventeen. I thought of myself as a high-school-age Barbara Walters, getting juicy interviews with a cross-section of the student body. No one was safe from me: jocks, cheerleaders, grinds, intellects, freaks. I would quote them and then write my own opinion of their activities.

Of course I wasn't always kind, and some of the things I said were slightly controversial. As a result, almost every week I had a fight with Mr. Harrington, our adviser—like the time he read my column on class do-gooders. I had said that do-gooders would even mop up the bathroom floors if they could put it on their college applications and get credit for being well-rounded students.

"Are you sure you want to write this Shelby?" That was Mr. Harrington's favorite remark.

"Are you telling me I can't write it, Mr. Harrington?"

"Just remember, Shelby, you can do a lot of damage to a person with a little gold pencil."

He was referring to a *real* little gold pencil. It had been a gift to me from Mom and Dad. It was attached by a chain to a tiny refillable notebook, and I carried it everywhere. I try to make the person I'm interviewing feel comfortable. No tape recorders or big notebooks—just this tiny pencil and pad that fit neatly into my pocket. It's amazing, but when people see the pencil they're caught off guard. I don't think they realize you can write just as much with a little pencil as with a big one.

Of course I *did* get plenty of "Why don't you drop dead and save us the trouble of drowning you?" letters after the publication of some of my columns. But if that was the price of freedom of the press, so be it.

Now I was angling for a column on L. Mark Compton, super-jock, *the* athlete at Union High. A six-foot-two senior with incredible black eyes and eyelashes, he had letters in football, basketball, and track.

When I cornered L. Mark after his basketball practice one evening, he said he'd give me a couple of minutes. He had just showered, and there were still some drops of water sparkling in his hair. We sat in the bleachers and talked about sports and team spirit, and he told me how great it was to play for good old Union. But that isn't what Barbara Walters would settle for, and neither would I.

"Mark," I said. "Really, the kids like to read personal stuff. You know, your favorite foods, rock stars, TV programs . . . stuff like that."

He hesitated. When he did speak, his voice was low and soft. But I wasn't supposed to be lulled by his voice. I was supposed to be concentrating on his words. If I didn't, Larry would say, "I told you so."

That's Larry Williams. He's a senior and editor-in-chief. We've been sort of going together this year. He keeps saying I've got the best chance at editor-in-chief because I'm completely professional. He also said I was the only one he'd trust to interview L. Mark Compton, because every other girl on the paper would immediately fall in love with him.

Mark stood up. "Listen, Shelby Dreighton, I've read some of the interviews you've done with other kids. I'm not about to give you any ammunition."

That annoyed me. Besides, I was beginning to feel uncomfortable. He was just so big standing there. Every once in a while our knees would touch, and those beautiful eyelashes were very distracting.

I looked down at my notebook. My little gold pencil had been drawing flower petals. I *never* doodle during interviews. I flipped to a fresh page.

"Everybody calls you Mark, but your name is L. Mark. Tell me, what's the first initial for?"

"No, you don't. That's my secret." He reached for his gym bag. "But I'm starving, and I'll buy you a burger. My car's in the lot."

That's how the interview began. In fact, it took a

while for it to end. It lasted through three evenings—*great* evenings, I should add. Of course I got a razzing from Larry, especially when I broke our weekly Friday night date to watch Channel 10's movie greats so I could sit in the bleachers and cheer for Union High and L. Mark Compton.

"I think you're falling for that guy, like every other girl in this school," Larry said.

"Wrong!" I retorted. "Didn't you ever hear of research?"

"Research at a basketball game?"

"If you want me to write about L. Mark Compton, I've got to observe him in his natural habitat, don't I?"

That Friday, after the game, I waited for L. Mark. When he came out of the locker room, he steered me out of the gym and out to the parking lot—through a maze of kids, including the cheerleaders, who lifted their eyebrows. I felt quite aglow from all the looks we got.

After going for pizza, we sat in front of my house in Mark's car and talked. He had his arm draped over the back of the seat and was talking in that low voice, and Barry Manilow was singing something on the radio—I don't know what. All I knew was that L. Mark was awfully near and that the music was making me feel very drifty. Mark was talking about the ocean, saying that he was a certified scuba diver and that every summer he worked on a university oceanography project. He wanted to major in marine biology in college. It really surprised me.

I don't know how I concentrated, though. The music kept sending vibrations through the car. Or maybe *I* was sending them. All of a sudden L. Mark leaned over and kissed me.

There are some things you can't report even if you *are* a super-objective reporter. I floated into the house, and all I know is that for the next few days, every time I heard Barry Manilow on the radio, my mind just seemed to drift away from whatever I was trying to concentrate on. Of course Larry noticed and started to kid me about it, and about the fact that I hadn't yet done my "Shelby Sez" column on L. Mark Compton.

"Don't worry," I said. "You'll have it on your desk by Friday."

The next day I waited for Mark outside the gym even though we didn't have a definite date. He walked out with some of the guys and sort of lit up when he saw me. "Hi, Shelby!" he said. "Hey, grab this, will you?" He had his gym bag in one hand and tossed me his loose-leaf notebook with the other—expecting *me* to carry it! I couldn't believe it! That did it. I'd had enough of Larry's taunts, for one thing, but for another I realized maybe Larry was right: Mark just took it for granted that every girl would fall for him. But not me.

He drove me home, and right in the middle of a Barry Manilow record, I leaned over and said, "C'mon, L. Mark. You know all my ambitions, and I know yours. Aren't you ever going to tell me what the L. stands for?"

He didn't even hesitate. Big, strong L. Mark trusted me. "Lancelot," he said.

"What? I don't believe it! Lancelot, like in King Arthur?"

"The same. My mother was a nut on lovers in literature. You know, Lancelot and Guinevere. So she promised herself that her first son would be named Lancelot. Luckily, my father insisted on adding Mark, too."

"Fantastic story." I leaned back against my seat.

"Maybe you're lucky she didn't fall in love with *Gone With the Wind*. She could have named you Rhett."

"I've thought of that. Or Cyrano, from *Cyrano de Bergerac*."

"Or Count Vronsky, from *Anna Karenina?*"

We played this game all the way home. I should have realized that we were picking only ill-fated lovers.

Lancelot Mark Compton never said a word when the "Shelby Sez" column appeared. It began with a question: "Guess what a fantastic three-letter athletic hero's first initial, L., stands for? Not love—though you'd think so, from the lineup of girls at the locker room—but for Lancelot! Please tell us, Lancelot Mark Compton: Could it be that Mark is really for Mark Antony, as in *Antony and Cleopatra?*"

He never said a word when he stood on the foul line that night and missed because the opponent's crowd was hooting "Lancelot, Lancelot, trot back home to Camelot. . . . "

He never said a word when his locker was decorated with big red paper kisses and sign saying, "To Lancelot, love from Guinny and all the other maids-in-waiting." As a matter of fact, he never said a word about it because Lancelot Mark Compton apparently had decided never to speak to me again.

I resumed my Friday nights at the TV movies with Larry, but it wasn't the same. First of all, Larry's kisses were getting a little too demanding. And frankly, they were boring. Kissing Larry had never been boring before. But of course I hadn't had L. Mark's kisses to compare them with. Larry couldn't help but notice. I tried to kiss him good-night with a little enthusiasm, but I couldn't manage it.

"Look, Larry," I finally said, "let's cool it a little, okay? I mean, we work well together on the paper, and I don't think we should mess up the relationship with all this other stuff."

"What's up, Shelby? Is it still Mark Compton? I thought that Lancelot column meant your crush was all over."

"There's nothing to be over 'cause there was never anything to begin with. Right now I'm just interested in becoming editor-in-chief and doing a good job for the paper."

"Okay by me." He zipped up his jacket.

I leaned over and kissed him on the cheek. Larry really was a nice guy, and I didn't want him to be mad. "You know, Larry, I'll tell you something if you promise not to laugh. Ever since I was a little girl, I've just wanted to be another Brenda Starr."

"Brenda Starr . . . like in the comics?"

"I know it's silly, but I always thought she was a real person and I wanted to be just like her, writing fabulous stories, being a famous reporter, traveling, wearing glamorous clothes, meeting mysterious men—the whole bit."

He opened the door. "Just think," he said. "When I was a little kid, I only wanted to be a fireman."

The next week, besides my column—in which I got in a dig about all the expensive student cars in the parking lot—I had to write a long, boring story about the guidance department. Larry excused me from putting the paper to bed, since I was already swamped with all the data from my research.

On Friday morning, when the paper came out, I didn't get to pick up my copy because I was busy making up labs I had missed while trying to make sense out of the guidance department. After lab, as I walked down the hall to my locker, I heard a lot of snickers and also noticed Paul Mann, one of the school's biggest nerds, standing near my locker with a bunch of his pals. They were all talking at once. I knew they were still mad about my story on them, in which I remarked that they gave Union some of the trashy aura of the New York Bowery.

"Well, if it isn't Brenda Starr. . . . " "Yeah, how ya doin', Brenda?" "Say, looking for a mystery man, Brenda?" "How about me?"

Paul got down on his knees. "Hey, Brenda, I'll put a patch on my eye if it'll turn you on."

"What are you talking about?" I asked, really annoyed. I took a step toward my locker. On the door was a note the size of a poster: "Dear Brenda: Never realized you wanted a little love in your life. I'll meet you tonight. Your mystery man."

The hoots got louder. One of the girls from the paper was going by, and I pulled her over. My cheeks were getting hot. I didn't like being laughed at. "Hey, Gail, what's going on?"

"Oh, Shelby!" she said, laughing. "Didn't you see your interview? It was a fabulous idea!"

"My interview? What are you talking about?"

Gail handed me the school paper and pointed to the "Shelby Sez" column. Instead of my story on the cars in the parking lot, there was a story about me! "That famous Union High School girl reporter—who, with her little gold pencil, cuts down personalities like a machete in a sugarcane field—has revealed to your editor-in-chief that she's always dreamed of being Brenda Starr. In fact, this girl reporter, obviously still arrested in an adolescent state, has even shown evidence lately that she would be receptive to a mystery man! Any mystery men out there? Your reporter awaits you. . . ." And so on. I felt sick. How could Larry take something I had told him privately and print it like that? And how could he distort it so much and make me look and sound like such a fool? I found my way to the girls' room. I didn't want to cry, but I couldn't help it. I flushed the toilet every time someone walked in so no one would hear me. I made myself wash my face, smile, grit my teeth, and last through a horrible day of taunts.

Late in the afternoon I passed Mark Compton. Well, I thought, I'm surely going to hear from him. He just smiled and said, "Hi, Shelby," as he passed by. That was the first time he had spoken to me since his interview.

I couldn't sleep the whole night. I had a lot of thinking to do: about interviewing people and making news at the expense of others.

Monday afternoon we had a newspaper staff meeting. I knew everyone was watching me, especially Larry and Mr. Harrington. I didn't say anything except when Larry asked if anyone had some new ideas to offer.

I raised my hand. "I've got one, Larry." I looked around the table "I'd like to do something different for the 'Shelby Sez' column. I'd like to spend some time each week actually participating in the activity of the person I'm writing about—like working with the prom committee, or practicing with the fencing club, or studying with the grinds.'"

There were murmurs around the table. Larry leaned over and whispered something to Mr. Harrington and then looked back at me.

"What exactly is the point, Shelby? First of all, it'd

take an awful lot of extra time, and second, I don't see how it could have any real impact on the column." Some of the other kids nodded.

I cleared my throat. "Well, what I have in mind is giving the column a new slant, some new life. But even more important, well . . . I've been doing a lot of thinking, and I have a feeling that if I were more *involved* in what I wrote about, maybe I'd really understand the things other kids are interested in—instead of just putting them down."

Mr. Harrington smiled, and I knew I had another winner.

"Okay, sounds good to me," Larry said. "Go to it."

When the meeting ended Larry walked over to me and held my arm. "So, what's the first 'new' column going to be about, Shelby?"

"It's going to be a surprise," I answered. I pulled my arm away, but gently. "I'll tell you this much, though: It *is* going to take lots of 'practice.' But don't worry about my meeting the deadline—I'm starting the story right away."

"Okay, I'm counting on you!" Larry said with a smile. He headed down the hall.

Before starting for my next class, I pulled out my little gold pencil and wrote a reminder to myself: "Talk to L. Mark's basketball coach about getting hold of an extra uniform, my size." Then I drew a little flower petal next to the note.

STATEMENT ON OUR HIGHER EDUCATION
FOR RON LAMPARD, NISQUALLY

We learned that you don't shoot
things that are wiser than yourself:
cranes, crippled bear, mountain beaver, toads.
We learned that a hunter who doesn't eat his game
is a traitor and should wander the earth,
starving, forever.
We learned to fish the shadow side of creeks
and to check traps every morning before the dew lifts.
It is a kindness in our savagery
that we learned to owe our prey
a clean death and an honorable end.
We learned from our game
to expect to be eaten when we die,
learned that our fathers
learned all this before us.
Because of this you are brother
to cranes, mountain beaver, toads and me.
And to one old crippled bear
that neither of us will ever see.

W. M. RANSOM

The
REBELLION
of the
MAGICAL RABBITS

A fable
by the Argentinian author
Ariel Dorfman

When the wolves conquered the land of the rabbits, the first thing the leader of the pack did was to proclaim himself King. The second was to announce that the rabbits had ceased to exist. Now and forever it would be forbidden to even mention their name.

Just to be on the safe side, the new Wolf King went over every book in his realm with a big black pencil, crossing out words and tearing out pictures of cottontails until he was satisfied that not a trace of his enemies remained.

But an old gray fox who was his counselor brought bad news.

"The birds, Your Wolfiness, insist that they have seen some . . . some of those creatures. From on high."

"So how come I don't see anything from way up here, on my throne?" asked the Wolf.

"In times like these," answered the fox, "people have got to see to believe."

"Seeing is believing? Bring me that monkey who takes photos, the one who lives nearby. I'll teach those birds a lesson."

The monkey was old and weak.

"What can the Wolf of all Wolves want with me?" he asked, looking at his wife and daughter.

The little girl had an answer. "He must want you to take a picture of the rabbits, Dad."

"Quiet, quiet," said her mother. "Rabbits don't exist."

But the little monkey knew that rabbits did exist. It was true that, since the howling wolves had invaded the country, the rabbits no longer came to visit her as they had before. But in her dreams she continued hearing the green rain of their voices singing nearby, reflecting in her head as if she were a pond under the moonlight, and when she awoke there was always a small gift beside her bed. Walls and closed doors were like water for the rabbits.

"That's why I sleep well," said the little girl. "That's why that General Wolf must need the photo. To keep nightmares away. You'll bring me a picture of them some-day, won't you, Dad?"

The monkey felt fear crawl up and down his fur. "Send this little girl to her room," he told his wife, "until she understands that there are certain things we just don't talk about."

The King of the Wolves was not in the best of moods when the monkey came in. "You're late. And I'm in a hurry. I need photographs of each important act in my life. And all my acts, let me tell you, are supremely impor-tant. . . . Can you guess what we're going to do with those pictures? You can't? We're going to put one on every street, inside every bush, in every home. I'll be there watching each citizen with my very own eyes. You'd better pity those who don't have the latest events of my life hung up on their walls. And you know who is going to distribute each picture? You don't know?"

The monkey was trembling so hard that no words came out.

"The birds, ugly monkey. Now they'll bite their own beaks before they twitter around with any nonsense about rabbits. And we'll tie an endless cord to their legs, so they can't escape. Understand?"

The monkey understood so well that his trembling paw immediately clicked the shutter of the camera, taking the first picture.

"Go," roared the Wolf, "and develop it. I want it on every wall in the kingdom."

But when the photographer returned some minutes later, he did not dare to enter the throne room, and asked one of the soldiers to call the counselor. Without a word, the monkey passed him the picture he had just taken.

The fox blinked once, and then blinked again. In a corner of the photo, far from the muscular, ferocious figure of the King—who had both arms up in the air as if he had just won a boxing championship—appeared what was without any doubt the beginning of an ear, the ear of someone who had insolently come to spy on the whole ceremony.

"You blind monkey!" fumed the fox. "How come you didn't notice that this . . . this thing was there? Can't you focus that camera of yours?"

"If it could get into the picture," the monkey answered, "it was because you and your guards let it get close."

"It won't happen again," the counselor promised. "Rub out that . . . ear before His Wolfishness finds out."

From his bag, the monkey took out a special liquid that he used to erase any detail that might bother a client. The intruding ear began to disappear as if it had never existed.

The King of the Wolves was pleased with the portrait and ordered it sent all over the realm. Two hours later he personally went on an inspection tour to make sure that not a window was without a picture of his large, gleaming, dangerous grin. "Not bad," he said, "but this photo is already getting old. People should see my latest deeds. Take another. Quick. Show me scaring these pigeons— right away. And bring it to me immediately. You took too long last time."

But the monkey wasn't able to comply this time either. Once again he had the counselor called secretly.

"Again?" asked the fox. "It happened again?"

Except that now it was worse than an indiscreet ear. A whole corner of the new picture was filled with the unmistakable face of . . . yes, there was no denying it, of a rabbit winking an eye in open defiance of the nearby guards.

"We've got to tighten security," muttered the fox. "Meanwhile, erase that invader."

"Wonderful," shouted the King Wolf when finally he was given the picture. "Look at the frightened faces of the pigeons trying to escape. I want a million copies. I want them on milk cartons and on the coupons inside cereals . . . Onward. Onward. Let's go and smash up a dam. Come on, monkey. Fame awaits us both."

The beavers had been working summer and winter for three years on a beautiful dam that would allow them to irrigate a distant valley.

The Wolf of Wolves climbed a tree. "I want you to

shoot the precise moment when my feet crash into the middle of the dam, monkey. If you miss the shot, next time I'll fall on top of you and then I"ll have to get myself another photographer. Are you ready?"

Not only was the monkey ready, so was the counselor. The fox was breathing down the old monkey's back, peering over his shoulder, watching, listening. Nothing could escape those vigilant, darting eyes. Not a fuzzy ear would dare to make its appearance.

So neither the monkey nor the fox could believe it when, a bit later, they saw at the bottom of the picture a rabbit lolling on his side as if he were relaxing at a picnic. Next to him, another rabbit had raised her paw and was boldly thumbing her nose.

"This is an epidemic," said the fox. "And let me tell you, our lives are in danger."

"Let's start erasing," the monkey said wearily.

"You erase. I'll get a squadron of buzzards and hawks. They see all animals, even the quick and the small."

His Wolfhood the King yelped with pleasure when he saw the picture. It portrayed him at the exact moment he was breaking the backbone of the beavers' dam. In the distance, families of beavers could be seen fleeing. There was not a single shadow of a rabbit.

"Send it out! A strong country is an educated country, a country that always is tuned in to the latest news. What are we going to do now for some fun?"

"We could rest," the monkey suggested, his paws peeling from the harsh erasing fluid.

The Wolf looked at him as if he were a stone.

"And who asked you for an opinion? I'm in charge here. That's why I was born with these teeth, and you'd better pray you never have to feel them crunching your bones. Onward. We are the future, the morrow, the dawn! We'll go on until there's no more light."

But in each new photo, the rabbits became more plentiful, audacious, and saucy. His Wolfinity the King destroyed sugar mills, shook squirrels out of their trees and hid their nuts, stripped ducks of their feathers, drove sheep off cliffs, drilled holes in the road so that horses would break their legs, unveiled new cages and old dungeons . . . and the more his frightening yellow eyes flickered, the more innumerable were the rabbits of every color that frolicked in the margins of the photographs. Even the clouds seemed full of fur and whiskers and cottontails.

"Hey, birdie," jeered the Supreme Wolf, grabbing a swallow about to fly off with bag overflowing with pictures, "what tune are you singing now, featherhead? Who's that in the center of the picture, huh? Who's the King?"

The bird held his beak tight, so that not even a peep could come out.

"Lights, camera, action, monkey!" the Monarch demanded. "Call this: WOLF KING RECEIVES HOMAGE FROM A MESSENGER."

The monkey obeyed, but could hardly hide his despair. Though nobody ever saw the rebels when the photos were taken, they were always there when it was time to show them, nibbling lettuce at the very feet of the biggest and baddest of wolves.

"Exterminate them," hissed the fox, who had ordered a stronger, more acid liquid. "Don't leave even a twitch of a nose."

But the pictures were beginning to look defective. There were blank spaces everywhere. The monkey knew that the only solution was to convince His Wolfishness to sit up high on an elevated throne. Since rabbits live underground, they wouldn't be able to wiggle their way into the frame of the photograph.

The King, fortunately, was delighted with the idea. "I'll look more impressive up here. And I can keep an eye on those birds. What a surprise for my subjects when they find my new picture at breakfast, right? So get here early, monkey, do you hear?"

When the exhausted monkey dragged himself home, his fingers hurting from the terrible liquid, the latest photograph of the King had just been plastered on the front door of his house. Just at that moment, a soldier was leaving.

"No cause for alarm, Mr. Monkey," the soldier laughed. "Just a routine inspection to see if anybody is sabotaging His Wolfhood's pictures."

The monkey rushed inside. "Our daughter? Is she all right? Did she say anything?"

"I'm fine, Dad," the little girl said. "Those wolves are gone, aren't they? And you brought me that special photo—you know, the one I asked you for?"

The monkey felt as if from all four walls, from all four pictures on the four walls, the eight eyes of the Biggest of Wolves were watching each word he might say.

"Let your father rest," said her mother. "The only pictures he's taken are the ones we've put up in the house, like good citizens."

But the next morning, the monkey was awakened by his child's kiss. She put her lips near his ears and whispered something so softly that only he could hear it: "Thank you. It's the best present you could ever give me. You're a magical dad."

"Thanks? Thanks for what?"

She motioned almost imperceptibly toward the wall from which the photo of the Wolf King ruled. Her father opened his eyes wide. In one of the corners of that picture, like the sun rising over the mountains, he could just glimpse, in the act of making their gradual but glorious appearance, a pair of, yes, of course, a pair of soft, pink, pointed ears.

The monkey jumped out of bed. The liquid he had applied did not work permanently. The rabbits had needed the whole night to sneak back into the pictures, but somehow they had managed it.

"I think they knew I was scared," the little girl murmured, "and came to see me while I slept."

Her father dressed in less time than it takes a chill to run up a spine and scurried to the palace without stopping for breakfast. Was this thing happening only at their house or could the same invasion have taken place everywhere in the kingdom? If so, how could the rabbits be removed from so many portraits?

His Wolfiness was still in bed, but the counselor was already pacing about, biting the tip of his tail. "It's a plague," he said, "but, fortunately, it is already under control. The offending pictures have been burned. As for you . . . "

"I swear that I—"

"Not a word from you," interrupted the fox. "It's lucky those creatures don't exist. Imagine the damage they'd cause if they really existed. But enough talk. What we need now is a new photo to replace the ones that are contaminated."

They rushed to the new throne, which was now set up on top of four colossal wooden legs, out of reach of the spreading virus of the mischievous ears.

"I want two shots," His Wolfhood demanded, "one

of me ascending my throne and another of me sitting on it, enjoying the fresh air. And send them abroad too, so those silly foreign papers will stop attacking me."

This time, when the photos were developed, there was no trouble. Not so much as a carrot of a sign of a rabbit.

"Didn't I tell you? Didn't I tell you they don't exist?" The counselor was jubilant. "It was just a matter of your focusing the camera properly."

For the next few days, there were no more unpleasant surprises. The Wolf of Wolves felt happy, high above the heads of the multitude. He let his lieutenants run things while he posed for pictures giving commands, delivering speeches, signing laws. He examined the shots carefully, however. "Congratulations," he said. "You're being more careful, monkey. It seems you're learning your trade just by being near me. I don't see any more of those whitish spots that spoiled my first pictures."

But one morning, the monkey was again awakened by his daughter's voice. "They're back, Dad," she whispered in his ears. "Those pictures you took sure are magical."

In one set of photos, at the foot of the towering throne, a small army of rabbits was biting, chewing, and splintering the wooden legs. Their teeth worked patiently, and they stopped their work only now and again to wave to the spectators.

The counselor was waiting. The monkey could see his fur ruffling and swelling like a swarm of bees.

"How many this time?" the monkey asked.

"The photos are being taken care of," the fox said grimly. "But the birds have got wind of what happened, and now they're telling everyone that those . . . those awful animals exist. And His Wolfinity is beginning to suspect something. 'Why are those birds so happy, so shrill?' he asks. I told him they're just a bunch of feather-brains, full of hot air."

"What did he answer?" asked the monkey.

The King had announced that balloons are full of hot air too and that they could be popped. If those birds didn't keep quiet, he would make them disappear.

But the counselor had another idea: The Wolf of All Wolves should tie a recording of one of his latest speeches around the necks of the birds. They would have to carry not only the photos, but also the King's words, all over his kingdom. Nobody would be able to hear any of their songs.

"Hearing is believing," trumpeted His Wolfiness. "We'll give them a taste of some hymns, some military marches, some lessons in history, economics, and ethics."

The old monkey's life became unbearable. Not even the recorded howls of the King and his chorus of warlike beasts could stop the timid appearance, in the next photo, of an inquisitive nose, a pair of furry ears, some white whiskers, and something hungry gnawing away at the legs of the throne.

The fox replaced the chief officer of the royal guard with a boa constrictor straight from the jungle of a neighboring country. He put small, hundred-eyed spiders in strategic places throughout the Wolfdom. One day he ordered half the population to shave off their shiny fur so that no spy could hide in it. To punish the cows, accused of uttering subversive moos, he commanded that their milk be soured. And finally, he raised the volume of the King's broadcasts. But in spite of these efforts, there began to be heard a persistent, rowdy, merry sound, the clicking of thousands of tiny teeth, the burbling of an underground stream.

The monkey felt dizzy.

The rhythm was maddening. During the night, the

legs of the throne, spindlier by the minute, were reinforced grudgingly by woodpeckers who would have much preferred to take the throne apart. The monkey had to rely on every photographic trick of the trade, now erasing, now trimming with scissors, disguising ears so they looked like shadows and shadows so they looked like wallpaper. He even began using old portraits of the King, trying to make them seem like recent ones.

Until one night, when it was very late, the old monkey was awakened by an angry hand that shook him from his slumber. It was the counselor, flanked by a fierce escort of soldiers. The Lord Wolf had sent for him.

The whole house was up by now. The little girl watched her father begin dressing.

"Say hello to His Foxcellency," said the monkey.

"Dad," she said, and it was astonishing that she did not speak in a low, fearful voice anymore, as if the armed guards were not even there, "today you've got to bring me that picture I asked for."

"A picture?" The counselor showed interest. "A picture of what, of whom?"

The child continued to ignore him. "Today you'll bring me a photo of the rabbits, right, Dad? For my wall?"

The mother monkey touched the girl's head as if she had fever. "Hasn't your father told you that rabbits don't exist? Haven't we shut you up in your room for telling lies?"

"They exist," the girl announced. "Everybody knows they exist."

"Just as I suspected," said the counselor. "Let's go."

The Wolfiest of Wolves was waiting for them atop his throne. Around each leg, hundreds of guards and snakes kept watch.

"Monkey, you are a traitor," thundered the King. "Your photos are being used by people who say that strange and malicious creatures—who are non-existent as everyone knows—are conspiring this very night to overthrow my rule. They say my throne trembles and my dynasty will topple. Is there any evidence that my throne trembles? Does anybody dare say so?" And he yowled like a hundred jet fighters in the air. "We'll start by making a recording of that sound. And you, you monkey, you're going to help me stamp out these rumors. Touching is believing. You are going to make me a wide-angle three-dimensional picture that will cover all walls. In color. Because I am going to crown myself Emperor of the Wolves, the Supreme Wolferor. And if a single wretched rabbit shows its snout, I will make you eat the photos, one by one, a million of them, and then I'll eat you and not only you, but your wife and your daughter, and all the monkeys in this country. Now. Take that picture."

The monkey stuck his quaking head under the black cloth behind his camera and focused on the throne. He let out a little moan. Up till then, the rabbits had appeared only later, when the picture was developed. But here they were now, directly in front of his lens, ungovernable and carefree, gnawing away, biting not only the wood of the throne, but also the swords of the astonished guards and the very rattles of the rattlesnakes.

"What's the matter?" bellowed the future Wolferor, who was not looking downward so his profile would be perfect for posterity.

The monkey moved the camera nearer the throne, hoping the rabbit army would not come out in the picture. The rabbits moved faster than he did. They were clambering up the legs, one on top of the other as if they were monkeys or birds. The soldiers tried to frighten them away in silence, unwilling to attract the attention of the King, but the invaders were too agile. The Wolves kept bumping into one another and hitting each other over the head. The monkey realized that a contingent of birds had arrived from above, winging freely through the air, without a cord tied to them or a recording.

"Hurry up!" ordered the Wolf of all Wolves.

The monkey closed his eyes very tightly. It was better not to witness what was going to happen. At the very moment he clicked the shutter, he heard a deafening noise. He knew what he was going to see when he opened his eyes, but still could not believe it: Like an old elm tree rotten to the core, the throne had come crashing to the ground along with the King of Wolves, guards, snakes, counselor, and all. The monkey blinked. There at the foot of his tripod lay the Biggest, Baddest, the Most Boastful Wolf in the Universe. His ribs were broken, his black fur was torn by the fall, his yellow eyes were reddened, and he was wailing in pain.

"Monkey," squeaked the would-be Wolferor of the World, "this picture . . . you have my permission not to publish it."

At that moment, all the lights in the palace went out. The monkey was paralyzed. He did not know where to go. Then, as if someone in the darkness were suddenly shining a light on a pathway, he knew what he must do. He grabbed his camera and his bag, and clutching them to his chest like a treasure, he fled.

His daughter was waiting for him at the door of the house.

"Wait," he said to her. "Wait. I've brought you something." And without another word, he raced into his darkroom to develop the last picture as quickly as possible.

When he came out a few minutes later, his daughter and wife were standing on chairs, taking down the pictures of the Wolf King.

"Here," the old monkey said to his daughter, blinking in the bright light. "Here, this is the picture you've been asking for all this time. I've finally brought you your present."

"Thanks, Dad," the little girl said. "But I don't need it anymore."

She pointed around the room and toward the street and across the fields where the sun was beginning to rise.

The world was full of rabbits.

THE SECRET

Jim told me a secret
   I shouldn't tell anyone,
But I told it to Julie
   Who thought that it was fun.
And Julie crossed her heart—
   She promised not to say—
But broke her word and told it
   The very next day.
She whispered it to Alex
   Who told it back to Jim
Who's mad at me for telling
   The secret on him.
And now I'm mad at Julie
   (She promised not to tell!)
And Julie's made at Alex,
   So mad that she could yell.
And Alex glared at Jim
   And said that he was twisted.
Then Jim came straight to me
   And said I would be fisted!
I hope all this blows over.
   I think it should, because
I've totally forgotten
   What the secret was!

ROBERT HEIDBREDER

About the Authors

Newspaper editor, novelist, playwright, and short story writer **Floyd Dell** (1887–1969) was part of the "Chicago School," a group of famous midwestern authors. He developed the "Literary Review" section of the *Chicago Evening Post* into a major newspaper supplement.

Charles de Lint was born in 1951 and became a Canadian citizen in 1961. He has worked as a retail clerk, a construction labourer, a publisher, and a columnist. He is best known for his contemporary fantasy stories and folk music.

The French writer **Guy de Maupassant** (1850–1893) is considered one of the finest short story writers of all time. Within a ten-year period, from 1880 to 1890, he published nearly 300 short stories and six novels, an amazing feat for any author.

Author, journalist, and scholar **Ariel Dorfman** was born in Argentina in 1942. In 1973 he was exiled from Chile, his adopted country, because of his outspoken resistance to the dictator, Augusto Pinochet. Since then he has taught at universities in France, the Netherlands, and the United States.

Barbara Girion was born in 1937 in New York City. She teaches writing to students of many ages and abilities. She began publishing her award-winning novels for young adults in 1978.

Born and educated in Illinois, the poet **Robert Heidbreder** is now a Canadian citizen and lives in Vancouver.

Monica Hughes, born in 1925 in England, travelled around the world before she settled in Canada and became a writer. She is best known for her science fiction novels, which are usually set in time periods just beyond the present. Hughes has won many awards for her writing for young adults.

Novelist and short story writer **Thomas King** is of Cherokee, Greek, and German descent. King teaches Native Studies at the University of Lethbridge in Alberta.

James Kirkup, born in England in 1927, divides his time living in that country, the United States, and Japan. Kirkup writes poetry continually. He has held positions in university English departments since 1950 and has translated scores of books for other writers.

W. M. Ransom, who is part Cheyenne and Arapaho, was born in the state of Washington in 1945. His poetry and stories have appeared in many journals and periodicals.

Peter D. Sieruta is a playwright, story writer, and librarian from

Michigan. The short story "Being Alive" is from his collection *Heartbeats and Other Stories*, first published in 1989.

Neil Simon is known as the most commercially successful playwright in Broadway history. Since 1960, there have been few Broadway seasons that did not feature one or more of his comedies or musicals. Simon was born in 1927 and lives in California and New York.

Budge Wilson, born in 1927 in Halifax, Nova Scotia, did not begin writing fiction for young adults until the age of fifty. She has also worked as an art and English teacher, librarian, filing clerk, staff artist, fitness instructor, newspaper columnist, and photographer.

Dyanoosh Youssefi escaped to Canada from Iran when she was twelve. She wrote "The Go Bus, a Boy and a Swastika" when she was nineteen. At the time she had just returned from Poland, where she took part in the "March of the Living," a memorial event for victims of the Holocaust.

Credits